ELECTRODYNAMIC MAN

Electromagnetic Field Measurements
in Biology, Medicine, Hypnosis
and Psychiatry

ELECTRODYNAMIC MAN

Electromagnetic Field Measurements
in Biology, Medicine, Hypnosis
and Psychiatry

Leonard J. Ravitz, M.S., M.D.

Edited by
The Hon. Edward W. Russell, O.B.E., M.A. (Cantab.)

Introduction by
F. S. C. Northrop, Ph.D., LL.D.

Rutledge Books, Inc.

Danbury, CT

Rutledge Books, Inc.
107 Mill Plain Road, Danbury, CT 06811
1-800-278-8533
www.rutledgebooks.com

Manufactured in the United States of America

Cataloging in Publication Data
Ravitz, Leonard J.
Electrodynamic Man

ISBN: 1-58244-210-X

1. Science

Library of Congress Catalog Card Number: 2002100357

Dedicated to the memory of:

The Hon. Edward W. Russell, O.B.E.,
M.A. (Cantab.), whose editorial
revisions made this book possible

About the Author

Leonard J. Ravitz, M.S., M.D., Diplomate American Board of Psychiatry and Neurology, Diplomate Board Certified Forensic Examiner, American Board of Examiners, Diplomate American Board of Forensic Medicine, American College of Forensic Examiners, Life Fellow American Psychiatric Association, Fellow American Association for the Advancement of Science, Fellow New York Academy of Sciences, Charter Fellow and Consultant in Certification Program American Society of Clinical Hypnosis and member Sigma Xi, was trained in hypnosis as a medical student by Milton H. Erickson, M.D. with whom he maintained a long friendship until Erickson's death in 1980. In the Section of Neuro-Anatomy laboratories at Yale Medical School, he studied neuroanatomy and field physics instrumentation monitoring techniques under Professor Harold S. Burr who directed Ravitz' electrodynamic field research and continued to follow it closely until Burr's death in 1973. Special training in epistemology, including the methodologic foundations of scientific knowledge and principles underwriting the application of field physics to basic problems in biology, medicine and psychiatry, was by Professor F. S. C. Northrop. This close association continued until Northrop's death in 1992. Following Yale, Ravitz was brought to Duke University School of Medicine and Hospital by Richard S. Lyman, M.D., where he completed his neuropsychiatric residency training. Since then he has worked at several places including the University of Pennsylvania School of Medicine and Hospital and Eastern State Hospital in Williamsburg, Virginia, where he was Director of Training and Research. Currently Dr. Ravitz practices psychiatry in New York City and Norfolk, Virginia.

Table of Contents

Acknowledgments

The teaching of hypnosis by Milton H. Erickson, M.D. and his counseling throughout the years until his death have proved of the greatest benefit to me. I am also indebted to Harold S. Burr, Ph.D., under whose guidance in his Yale Medical School laboratories my experiments were inaugurated. Likewise over the years, F.S.C. Northrop, Ph.D., LL.D., provided critical understanding of the basic assumptions underwriting these experiments as well as important counseling. The material help and encouragement of Richard S. Lyman, M.D., and Katharine R. Lyman must also be acknowledged, as well as the equally long-term support of Elias F. Mengel, Ph.D., John P. Craig, M.D., M.P.H., Elizabeth M. Erickson and Barbara K. Russell. Frank A. Pattie, Ph.D., introduced me to the protoplastic work of the great 18th-century British physician, Richard Mead. Hallowell Davis, M.D., reviewed the EEG and furnished a succinct editorial condensation of the hypnotically revivified seizure section. Much of the illustrative material derives from the photography of Taylor B. Lewis Jr. and Robert V. Fischbeck. I am also grateful for the chart produced by Randolph Bruce and the careful review of this manuscript by Kenneth A. Bartlett Jr., D.D.S., and Horace G. Oliver Jr., M.A. Berthold E. Schwarz, M.S., M.D., Louis Langman, M.D., Wm. F. Blair, M.D., and Paul F. Kost, Ph.D., M.D. also provided valuable suggestions. The statistical studies of Chester R. Wilpizeski, Ph.D., and Ralph Markson, M.S., Ph.D., and the editorial assistance of Sunday D. Abbott, M.S., in preparing it for publication are all deeply appreciated. I wish to express my gratitude to Paul D. MacLean, M.D., and David B. Cheek, M.D., for their suggestions and support. Finally, I would like to thank Thomas P. Higgins, Esq. for his assistance in seeing this volume through the publication process.

Foreword

Human emotions can now be *measured* with a voltmeter. And we owe this historic discovery to the author of this important book, Dr. Leonard J. Ravitz.

For many years, Dr. Ravitz was a pupil and friend of Dr. Harold Saxton Burr. He is, therefore, a living link with the co-discoverer of the electrodynamic fields which organize and maintain *all* living forms through constant changes of material. This solution of what was formerly one of life's greatest mysteries is of the highest medical, philosophical and even political importance.

Dr. F.S.C. Northrop and Dr. Harold Saxton Burr first advanced *The Electro-Dynamic Theory of Life* in 1935. Few, if any, theories have had a more solid mathematical foundation and experimental proof. Yet few great discoveries have ever received so little attention.

Here, at last, is a book which describes the origin of the *Theory*, its experimental proof and its vast importance to humanity. And, as one who has closely followed Burr's work since the beginning, no one is better qualified to write this book than Dr. Ravitz. He is more familiar with this work than any man alive.

This book, therefore, is a "must" reading for all doctors, biologists, plant-breeders and philosophers. It is of importance to all interested in knowing that man is an *electrodynamic organization,* a *purposeful* part of an organized universe and subject to its laws and forces. It is an invaluable contribution to the history of science.

As a discoverer himself, of course, the author is much more than a historian. He is the first man in history to demonstrate that the state of the mind has *measurable effects* on the organizing electrodynamic field of the body and, conversely, this field has *measurable effects* on the mind. As far back as 1948, he was able to measure the depth of hypnosis with a sensitive voltmeter. He has since discovered that it is possible to measure emotions, *even past emotions recalled under hypnosis.*

These discoveries are of paramount importance to psychologists, psychiatrists and all interested in mental health. They have practical implications, too, for industry and the Armed Forces because they make it possible to detect *in advance* emotional instability.

This is a "dual-purpose" book. While it is scientific enough to appeal to—and to instruct—the most meticulous scientists and research workers, the author includes explanations which anyone can understand.

Nonscientific readers can easily skip passages in unavoidably scientific language. They will have no difficulty in following the history—and appreciating the importance—of the great American discovery of the *electrodynamic fields of life.*

No one interested in the true nature of man can afford to ignore it.

The Hon. Edward W. Russell, O.B.E., M.A. (Cantab.)
Former Managing Editor and General Manager
The Morning Post (London, England)

About the Editor

The Hon. Edward W. Russell, O.B.E., M.A. (Cantab.) who died on February 13, 1982, at the age of 80, had the distinction of making significant contributions in a number of areas of life not normally thought to overlap—among them science, the military, diplomacy and Fleet Street.

He was born in India in 1901, the third son of Lord Ampthill who was then Governor of Madras and Viceroy.

Soon after graduating in engineering and chemistry from Cambridge, Edward Russell developed a method of growing Piezo crystals and built and patented the first hi-fi system using crystal pick-up.

A talent for lucid writing and an insatiable curiosity about people led him to leave science for a period and turn to journalism. He became a reporter, then feature and leader writer for the Daily Express before moving to The Morning Post, where he became managing editor and general manager.

His fifteen years on Fleet Street were interspersed with investigative assignments to America, South Africa and India.

On the outbreak of World War II, he was commissioned in the RAF and assigned to research on radar and also to find and recruit suitable scientists in Canada and America.

After Pearl Harbor, he was appointed to the British Joint Staff Mission in Washington, D.C., where he also acted as Public Relations Officer for the Royal Air Force in the United States.

Released at the end of the war with the rank of Wing Commander, he turned again to science and spent some years on chemurgy research, particularly on the development of alcohol fuels, a project which he later said was "at last being considered seriously, twenty-five years too late."

This research period was interspersed with spells on various official bodies—he was Deputy Chief of Mission for the World Bank mission to Cuba—and with authorship.

A friend of Dr. H. S. Burr, E. K. Hunt, Professor of Anatomy at Yale, Russell became convinced that Burr had produced incontrovertible scientific evidence of an energy field associated with all life-forms, this field having, to a significant extent, the properties reported by mystics in all ages.

Because Burr could not publish such "vitalist" findings without prejudice to his status in the scientific establishment, Russell, with Burr's cooperation, popularized the data in *Design for Destiny* (London 1971). Shortly before Burr's death, he edited Burr's own book, *Blueprint for Immortality* (London 1972, 1977, 1982, 1988). This was published in America as *The Fields of Life* (1973).

Quotations from both these books appear increasingly nowadays in areas of science which are moving away from the materialistic and reductionist standpoints.

Russell's later publications include *Report on Radionics* (London 1973) and *Prospects of Eternity* (London 1982).

At the time of his death, Russell was working on a transistorized device based on Burr's electrodynamic fields which would give an instant indication of ovulation, a birth-control method free from drugs and current unreliable procedures.

Edward Russell was a giant of a man, physically, mentally and emotionally. His generosity was legendary but always covert. He is known to have handed over all the rights in more than one invention merely because he took an instant liking to someone who was interested.

To those who knew him intimately, he will be remembered for his huge capacity for friendship and for the joking twinkle which he embedded in almost every sentence. Outside his personal circle, he may well continue to be remembered for Russell's law: "The resistance to new ideas increases by the square of their importance."

Edward Campbell

Some principal publications of Editor Edward W. Russell:

1968. The discoveries of Burr and Ravitz: A new way to test personnel. *The Pentagon Seminar "Techniques of Personnel Assessment,"* L. M. Ehrmann, ed. Washington, DC: Office of the Secretary of Defense, pp. 121-125.

1971. *Design for Destiny: Science Reveals the Soul.** North American paperback edition 1973. New York & Toronto, Ontario, Canada: Ballantine.

1972, 1977, 1982, 1988. *Blueprint for Immortality: The Electric Patterns of Life.** Authored by Harold S. Burr & edited by E. W. C. Russell, no credit given.

1973. *The Fields of Life: Our Links With the Universe.* North American paperback edition New York & Toronto, Ontario, Canada: Ballantine.

1973. *Report on Radionics: Science of the Future. The Science which can cure where Orthodox Medicine Fails.**

1982. *Prospects of Eternity: Debunking Death.**

*All books published by Neville Spearman Ltd., London and Sudbury, Suffolk, England, bought by the C. W. Daniel Co. Ltd., 1 Church Path, Saffron Walden, Essex CB10 1JP, England.

Introduction

It was the genius of Harold Saxton Burr (1889-1973) to find the appropriate apparatus for measuring the electrodynamic field factor in all living creatures, both plants and animals.

With absolute singleness of mind, and with the aid of other scientists* who knew the fundamental field equations and their operational definitional implications, Burr developed the appropriate Gibbsian relational potential electrodes and high-input impedance experimental apparatus necessary for masking the particle physics factor, thus making it possible to single out and measure with continuously recorded day and night readings the electrodynamic field factor in plants and animals, including also neuropsychological normal and disturbed human beings.

Starting in 1948, Burr directed the research of Dr. (M.D.) Leonard Ravitz in the Yale University Graduate and Medical Schools who made the first electromagnetic field measurements of hypnosis and showed that not only hypnotic depth, but also the strength of emotions, could be objectively measured with the Burr-Lane-Nims millivoltmeter developed by Burr and others. Later, somatic states were similarly measured by Dr. Ravitz.

For the first time in medical science, this made possible a trustworthy, scientifically objective and verifiable science of interpersonal psychology and psychiatry. Differences in the time-flow changes in the field physics Maxwellian equational potentials when compared for people under and not under hypnosis provided objective criteria for the short-range psychiatric diagnosis and/or prognosis. An objective electronic assessment of emotional and physical states was developed, basing both on a single regulating principle defined in terms of measurable field intensity and polarity changes.

* H. S. Burr, Ph.D., Comparative Zoology, Yale University, and E.K. Hunt Professor of Anatomy in the Yale Medical School was guided by Professor Cecil T. Lane via Maxwell's equations to the electromagnetic electrometers, and by Professor Leslie F. Nims of the Department of Physical Chemistry to the silver-silver chloride, Gibbsian relational theory of potential electrodes.

As an introduction to *The Electro-Dynamic Theory of Life*, written by Burr and me in 1935, let me present the concrete inductive comparative neurozoological considerations which led to its writing.

Before Burr had turned to the inorganic science of field physics , he made a very important natural history discovery with regard to Amblystoma's (salamander's) later stages which was published in the *Journal of Comparative Neurology*, 1924, 37: 455-479 entitled "Some experiments on the transplantation of the olfactory placode in Amblystoma." Shortly thereafter, in 1931, the present writer described its import as follows:

> Desirous of increasing the number of olfactory nerves for a certain experiment which he had in mind, he [Burr] added some olfactory nerve tissue to the normal supply of a certain organism. He was surprised to find that in over fifty percent of the cases the transplanted tissue did not grow along the normal olfactory nerve path. Instead, it wandered off through the brain case into the central nervous system by an entirely original route. He suggests that the explanation is to be found in Child's theory of the physiological gradient.* Due to changed conditions at the time when the experiment was performed, the distribution of gradient differences was not the same as when the original olfactory nerve was laid down...In any event, we have experimental evidence that nerve tissue can develop in mature differentiated organisms along entirely new lines.

This experimental discovery, as well as the bioelectric measurements of living matter, had two important consequences. First, they prepared the way for Burr's later E. K. Hunt Professorship of Anatomy in the Yale Medical School. Second, they marked the beginning of his transition from traditional, descriptive, natural history methods of scientific inquiry to one based on the theory and mathematics of field physics characterized by its many-entity terms

* Child's experminents showed that external factors, such as light rays, for example, create regional differences in the living system which tend to orient the formal arrangement of the internal material relative to these differences. Child called these regional diferences the physiological gradient. Child's work demonstrates that the form of living things is determined not only by heredity and internal physico-chemical constituents, but by external influences as well. The field of nature in which an organism is embedded plays an important role in its biological organization.

and relational, field-continuum, mathematical, equationally defined and deductively formulated theory. The immediate result was that Burr suggested that he and I write the paper published in the *Quarterly Review of Biology*, 1935, 10: 322-333 entitled *The Electro-Dynamic Theory of Life*. He was to do the experimental operational verification; I the theoretical field physics part.

By applying the operational instruments entailed by *The Electro-Dynamic Theory of Life* to maple, elm and oak trees for some three decades between 1943 and 1973, Burr found positive and negative polarities and sudden shifts of polarities occurring and recurring continuously in recorded day and night readings. These variations coincided with the phases of the moon and the distant sun's electromagnetic field radiation. The trees showed a constant isomorphic field potential variability when compared with sunspot data over this thirty-year period collected by Ralph Markson, Ph.D., then a graduate student of the Pennsylvania State University and now at the Massachusetts Institute of Technology. The same isomorphism was verified by the Yale University Professor Edmond Sinnott for the spatial relatedness of his three-dimensional Cucurbita. In 1935, potentials and polarity differences in various varieties of seed corn were measured for U. S. Secretary of Agriculture Henry Wallace. Vigorous seeds were distinguished from weak ones, ensuring planting of the former and thus increasing the production of corn the world over.

With animals, Burr measured the field potentials of the fertilized egg of Amblystoma from the single-celled fertilized egg through all of its many-celled experimental, morphological, developmental stages as described in the paper by Professor Ross Harrison of Yale's Zoology Department. The Amblystoma's first stage, when the Burr-Lane-Nims electrodes were applied, was dramatic. In this first fertilized stage, the Amblystoma was to the naked eye but a spherical white homogenous egg, yet the electrodes indicated definite polarities. Furthermore, in a later state, the lip of this creature, which initiated its nervous system, appeared at the positive pole, which had been indicated by measurements in Stage I. Clearly, neurophysiological differentiation was following the antecedent electrodynamic polarization.

Following the long-term confirmation of *The Electro-Dynamic Theory of Life* for Amblystoma; maple, elm and oak trees; seed corn and Cucurbita, other medical colleagues pursued the experimental implications of field physics measurements in determining ovulation, first in rabbits and then in women. Drs. R. T. Hill and Edgar Allen in the Yale Medical School, using the electrodynamic apparatus and electrodes, discovered ovulation periods in the rabbit and published their findings in the *Proceedings of the Society of Experimental Biology and Medicine*, 1935, 33:109-111. This led, naturally, to further research by Burr with the experimental psychologist C. I. Hovland in the Yale Medical School on bioelectric potential gradients in the chick, *Yale Journal of Biology and Medicine*, 1937, 9: 247-258. Then followed field potential readings of childless women which specified the best period of insemination based upon the prediction of the occurrence of ovulation. These experiments, performed with the obstetricians Drs. Luther K. Musselman, D. Martin, N. Kelley and Louis Langman led to husband and wife, in several cases, producing a child when none had come previously over many years. Similarly, Burr, Dr. Louis Langman and other collaborating doctors have used electrical field physics potential difference readings to detect malignant cell division in patients.

Thus, Burr, Ravitz and others have affirmed the crucial role of polarity in determining basic biological processes including morphogenesis, growth, ovulation, injury, wound healing, malignancy, aging, psychological disturbances and somatic disorders.

This polarity, which is characteristic of the electrodynamic field, necessitates the science of field physics as the theoretical basis of life. However, *both* the Faraday-Maxwell field physics component *and* the Newtonian particle physics component constitute all living vegetation, animate and human beings, as well as all inorganic systems. The particles in biological organization both determine and are oriented by the electrodynamic field.

A mathematical theory describing this interaction is essential and has been necessitated by the work of both Ravitz and José Simões da Fonseca, Ph.D., M.D., Faculdade de Medicina de Lisboa, whose 1970-published tripartite logic is a mathematical articulation of neurocybernetic-information factors.

Dr. Ravitz has extended his work to embrace not merely a field physics theory of hypnosis, but also to include in its theoretical basis the important role of memories—the "trapped reverberating universals" of McCulloch, Pitts, von Domarus and Fonseca. This will be described later in this volume by Dr. Ravitz himself. It now remains to develop a mathematical theory making it possible to compare and relate the Burr-Ravitz nonspecific electromagnetic field measurements in biology and medicine, including behavior disorders, with Fonseca's specific, relational, neurocybernetic-information, tripartite systems approach to psychology and psychiatry.

Since Dr. Burr's death in 1973, his work has been carried on principally by Dr. Ravitz. We shall look then to him and to his fellow scientists to show us the way. Led by Harold Saxton Burr, their work, to paraphrase A. E. Housman's *A Shropshire Lad*, may do more than Milton can to teach the natural ways of God to man.

F. S. C. Northrop, Ph.D., LL.D.
Sterling Professor
Philosophy and Law
Yale University

About Dr. Northrop

Filmer S. Northrop, Ph.D., LL.D., Sterling Professor Emeritus Philosophy and Law, Yale University, gained international renown for his books, *Science and First Principles* (Cambridge University Press and Macmillan 1931) and *The Meeting of East and West* (Macmillan 1946). For his chapter on Mexican culture in the latter book, he was awarded the Order of the Aztec Eagle by the Mexican government in 1949. In a front page *New York Times* book review, July 7, 1946, Howard Mumford Jones said it was "...the most important intellectual event in the United States thus far in 1946." *The Meeting of East and West* was reprinted ten times and translated into three languages.

Supreme Court Justice William O. Douglas said of another of Professor Northrop's books, *Philosophical Anthropology and Practical Politics: A Prelude to War or to Just Law* (Macmillan 1960), that it belongs "...in the small select list of the most important writings of this century."*

Northrop had the rare distinction of being appointed to an endowed Sterling professorship in both philosophy and law and was one of the few nonlawyers to teach at Yale Law School. He was chair of the Department of Philosophy from 1938 to 1940 as well as the first Master of Silliman College (one of the Yale residential colleges), from 1940 to 1947.

One of the many highlights of Professor Northrop's career was his study of the Theory of Relativity to determine the nature of scientific methods.

Northrop met Albert Einstein in 1927 at the University of Berlin, and subsequently consulted with him regularly until Einstein's

* The Papers of W.O. Douglas, Library of Congress Manuscript Division, Speeches and Writings File, 1928-79, Container No. 1090, 1960-61, Washington, D.C.: book review of *Philosophical Anthropology and Practical Politics* by F.S.C. Northrop sent for publication to Margaret Rennert, *The Washington Post*, by his secretary, Fay Aull, Sept. 17, 1960. Published caption, "Paths Away from the Abyss." Sunday, September 25, 1960, p. E6, cols. 1-2, Library of Congress: James Madison Bldg. 133.

death in 1955. In the book *Albert Einstein: Philosopher-Scientist,* Einstein commented:

> The essays by Lenzen and Northrop both aim to treat my occasional utterances of epistemological content systematically...Northrop uses these utterances as point of departure for a comparative critique of the major epistemological systems. I see in this critique a masterpiece of unbiased thinking and concise discussion, which nowhere permits itself to be diverted from the essential.*

* Reply to criticisms: Remarks concerning the essays brought together in this cooperative volume, p. 683. Translated from the German transcript by Paul Arthur Schilpp. *Library of Living Philosophers,* v.7. Open Court and Cambridge University Press, 1949.

Chapter One

A Great American Discovery

1

Any basic discovery which sheds new light on the true nature of human beings is obviously of the highest medical, psychologic and philosophic importance and in theory, such a discovery should be hailed with enthusiasm by all concerned. In practice, however, it is likely to encounter either indifference or opposition from entrenched or prejudiced professionals. That is why, historically, it has taken about forty years for new ideas to become accepted in the medical world.

This was realized by no less a scientist than Max Planck, who once observed:

> A new scientific truth does not triumph by convincing its opponents and making them see the light but rather because its opponents eventually die and a new generation grows up that is familiar with it.

The purpose of this book is to tell a new and unprejudiced generation about the nature and significance of a breakthrough discovery in biologic science which was made in 1935.

Briefly, this discovery is that man is an electric organization, an inseparable part of a universe of law and order. He is *not*—as some have supposed—the accidental consequence of the random association of molecules or of haphazard evolution.

It has long been known that the materials of which the human body is composed are constantly renewed in the same form and biologists were unable to explain the mystery of this organization.

Since the early 20th century, the mystery—and the bafflement of the biologists—deepened when the use of "tagged" elements revealed that the process of renewal is more rapid and complete than had previously been realized.

It was found that there is a complete turnover of all the material of the human body every six months and that some organs are completely renewed even more frequently. What keeps them "in shape" through all this ceaseless metabolism and change of material?

The mystery was solved by the discovery that the human body —and, indeed, *each* living form—is organized, directed and maintained by a primary electrodynamic field which in part controls the subsidiary fields associated with the organism's component parts.

This electrodynamic field is an electronic corset or straightjacket which literally "keeps us in shape" through perpetual alterations of material. It is of the same nature as the electromagnetic fields known to physics, though far more complex, and can be measured and mapped with sensitive micro and millivoltmeters.

Here the terms "electrodynamic," "electromagnetic," and "quasi-electrostatic" fields can be used interchangeably. The important point is that fields arc being measured, any distinctions in terminology being determined by the instruments used in making the measurements.

Though there is some feedback to the field from the form it controls, the field is primary and dominant and certain measurable variations in the field often anticipate physical conditions. Female ovulation, for example, can be detected by electronic measurements of the field. By the same method, some forms of cancer can be detected before there are any overt symptoms.

The human body, then, is the product of an organizing field which, in common with all other fields, is within, and subject to, the greater organizing fields of the Universe. In short, man is no accident.

2

We owe this epochal discovery to the genius of two Americans, Filmer Stuart Cuckow Northrop, B.A., M.A., Ph.D., LL.D. (1893-1992) and Harold Saxton Burr, Ph.D. (1889-1973). Dr. Northrop was to become Sterling Professor of Philosophy and Law at Yale University and Dr. Burr was to become E. K. Hunt Professor of Anatomy in Yale University School of Medicine.

Together they catapulted man into what we may call the Field Age. Their first shot—which, regrettably, was not "heard around the world"—was publication of *The Electro-Dynamic Theory of Life* in 1935, which stated:

> The pattern or organization of any biological system is established by a complex electro-dynamic field which is in part determined by its atomic physio-chemical components and which, in part, determines the behavior and orientation of those components. This field is electrical in the physical sense and by its properties relates the entities of the biological system in a characteristic pattern and is itself, in part, a result of the existence of those entities. It determines and is determined by the components.
>
> More than establishing pattern, it must maintain pattern in the midst of a physio-chemical flux. Therefore, it must regulate and control living things. It must be the mechanism, the outcome of whose activity is wholeness, organization, and continuity.

This was the first biologic theory of the century based on Einstein's relativity field physics and Maxwell's electromagnetic field equations.

With this sound theoretic basis for their proposition and with the aid of other scientists familiar with the field physics equations and their implications, Burr was able to devise the instruments and electrodes necessary to detect and measure the electrodynamic fields which he and Northrop had suggested exist in *all* living forms, from men to mice, from trees to seeds.

An electrodynamic or electromagnetic field is a continuum of experimentally verifiable vector forces defined in terms of two parameters: magnitude or intensity, **E** and direction or polarity, **H**.

To demonstrate the presence of electrodynamic fields in living matter, therefore, the instruments had to be capable of measuring voltage gradients having both intensity and directional properties, i.e., plus or minus polarity.

This in itself was no small achievement, involving many hours of tedious experiment. By modern standards, the electronic equipment available to them in those days was primitive. Vacuum tubes were not so precisely manufactured and pairs had to be matched. Recording galvanometers were not as reliable and stable as they are today. Of course, transistors were unknown. They had great trouble designing instruments and circuitry which could operate repetitively and reliably.

In addition, measurement of voltage gradients in living systems required the ability to measure potential differences. Willard Gibbs had long ago pointed out that in fluid systems—and all living creatures are fluid systems—it is impossible to measure a potential at a point. Only potential differences between two points, both of which may be changing, can be measured. What is measured, therefore, is not a specific value, but the differences between any two points measured.

It was Burr's genius which overcame these complex challenges along with the help of other scientists, particularly Northrop and subsequently, the Maxwellian experimental expert, Yale physics professor Cecil T. Lane, Ph.D., and the Yale-Brookhaven Gibbsian physical and physiologic chemist, Leslie F. Nims, Ph.D. Together they invented the first Burr-Lane-Nims high-input impedance, high sensitivity milli and microvoltmeters, with appropriate relational, reversible, nonpolarizing silver-silver chloride fluid-junction electrode pickup *for masking such factors as current flow and resistance without disturbing the system being measured.*

A theoretic operational procedure, suggested as feasible in the light of Maxwell's field equations, dictated an empiric operational procedure. This involved the development of sensitive vacuum tube potentiometers to create, in effect, balanced Wheatstone bridge circuits. As a result, anatomist Burr, physicist Lane and physical chemist Nims designed high-input impedance (10 megohms and above) micro and millivoltmeters which could measure pure voltage gradients independently of changing current flow and resistance, with minimal current drain (10^{-12} amperes) from the tested object. Only in this way could the variables of Ohm's law be isolated and the electric fields be measured accurately.

Cecil T. Lane designed the micro and millivoltmeters. Leslie F. Nims devised the special electrodes. These electrodes were made of a fine silver wire or rod of any suitable dimension which was chlorided by electrolysis in HCl solution or, following the suggestion of Dr. Theodore Shedlovsky, Rockefeller Institute, the silver wire was dipped into molten silver chloride. Electrode size depended on the organism being measured. Between the electrodes and the surface of the organism, a bridge of saline was used so that no metal contacted the measured object.

The electrodes had to be made in sizes small enough to measure the voltage gradients in seeds, frogs' eggs, and even slime molds. In addition, the instruments had to be capable of measuring minute, slowly changing voltage differences without disturbing the system being measured. Those familiar with the difficulties can only marvel at the patience, persistence and skill of these men.

This paid off. They were able to detect and measure the field in a great variety of living forms, botanic as well as zoologic.

On a small scale, one of Burr's most elegant demonstrations was to float a living salamander in a saline-filled circular dish. Immersed in the solution were electrodes connected to a recording galvonometer. The electrodes were able to detect the field of the salamander as it rotated *between* them and produced a perfect sine wave curve on the recorder which continued at lesser intensities as the electrodes were moved away from the creature, thus showing that its field properties radiated throughout the surrounding medium. A rotating copper solder robot, which usually produces a voltage gradient because of the bimetallic components, showed identical results whereas no electric output was noted by a rotating inert glass rod control. This makes it clear that existing field properties of the salamander could be recorded at a distance from the creature itself and, as with the simple fields of physics, could produce an effect across a space or gap.

On a larger scale, perhaps his most dramatic and philosophically important experiment was to measure the fields of maple, elm and oak trees in New Haven and Lyme, Connecticut, day and night for over thirty years. Analysis of the continuous electrometric recordings showed that the fields varied diurnally, weekly, with the phases of the moon, seasonally and semiannually. Comparison with sunspot data also showed that the fields of the trees responded annually to variations in the sunspot cycle.

It is obviously impossible to keep a human being hitched to a recording millivoltmeter continuously for many years. But if moon phases and sunspots can affect the electromagnetic fields of trees, it is reasonable to suppose that they might also affect the more complex human fields.

In sharp contrast to the fields of giant maple trees, Burr measured the fields in samples of former Secretary of Agriculture Henry

Wallace's seed corn. He was able to distinguish the more vigorous seeds from the seeds of weaker specimens, a finding subsequently verified when the seeds were planted. The highest voltage seeds grew more rapidly and had the best yields. The lowest voltage seeds were scrawny and grew the slowest. He was also able to demonstrate a significant relationship between the electrodynamic field patterns of young fruits and the ultimate shapes of their gourds.

Burr's curiosity was as insatiable as his industry was prodigious. He made field measurements with mice and rabbits and was even able to get voltage gradient correlates with all the many-celled development changes of Amblystoma, or salamander, beginning with its single-celled fertilized egg.

Burr was inspired to try this technically difficult experiment by an important neurologic discovery he had made before he turned to field physics. In an attempt to increase the number of olfactory nerves in the salamander, Burr added some olfactory nerve tissue to it. To his surprise he found that in over 50% of cases, the transplanted tissue did not grow along the usual nerve paths but wandered off through the brain into the central nervous system by an entirely different route—experimental evidence that nerve tissue *can* develop in mature, differentiated creatures along entirely new lines. This experimental discovery paved the way for Burr's future E. K. Hunt Professorship of Anatomy and inspired him to substitute a measurable electrodynamic field for Childs' purely physiologic gradient theory as a controlling factor in the development and growth of living systems.

This experiment with the neurology of the humble salamander was the first step in the long journey of discovery which revealed the existence of electrodynamic fields in all living forms. With his colleagues and research students, Burr progressed from the study of animals to the study of men and women. This steady progress was marked by the publication of such diverse papers as: "Detection of ovulation in the intact rabbit," "Bio-electric potential gradients in the chick," and "A Bio-electric record of human ovulation."

With other doctors, Burr was able to show from his measurements of the EMF (electromotive force or voltage gradients) of women the best period for insemination in cases where insemination had not been effective before. Likewise, with collaborating doctors, Burr discovered that field measurements can detect malignancy.

I was privileged to be a pupil of Burr. Working at first with Burr and later alone, I was able to show that continuous readings make it possible to distinguish between healthy men and women and those suffering from psychologic disturbances. In 1948, I was also able to demonstrate that the depth of hypnosis can be measured by characteristic variations in the field.

All these achievements of Burr and his colleagues—and many more equally important to be described later—speak for themselves.

Despite the obvious importance of *The Electro-Dynamic Theory of Life* it would be as wrong to claim too much for it as too little. We must remember that in addition to field physics, there is also particle physics.

Burr and Northrop emphasized from the outset that particles in biologic organization both determine and are oriented by the electrodynamic field. In other words, there is a reciprocal causal relationship between fields and particles.

How to relate them in inorganic, biologic and psychologic science is one of today's and tomorrow's most important scientific and philosophic challenges.

3

To digress for a moment for the benefit of those interested in history, modern theories of field physics and particle physics are not as new as some may suppose. In fact, they have ancient and distinguished origins. It was the deductive thinking of the ancient Greeks that founded this subject.

For instance, the particle physics acoustics of Democritus were formalized in Book VII of Euclid's *Elements*, while the General Theory of Ratios and Proportions of Eudoxus was given in Euclid's Book V. The five regular solids of stereometry deduced by Theaetetus were expounded in Euclid's Book XIII along with the mathematical astronomy of Hipparchus and Eudoxus. The word "physiology," derived from the Greek, emphasizes the importance of a mathematical approach because, literally, it means "the logic of nature."

From these examples we can see that field physics is as ancient as particle physics. As the distinguished experimental and theoretic spectroscopist, Professor S. Sambursky, tells us:

> The continuum theory of Anaxagoras with the postulate that 'there is a smaller but never a smallest'—which is necessary for all the proofs in Book X of Euclid's *Elements* and its presence in the field physics of the stoic physicist Chrysippus—anticipates modern 19th century infinitesimal mathematics and the Faraday, Maxwell, and Einstein field theory. Also, it is as indispensable as is the atomism of Democritus and the biologist Empedocles, the particle physics of Newton's *Principia*, Dalton's chemistry, the Brownian Movement, the kinetic theory of heat and gases, the physiological chemistry of Lavoisier, Henderson's steady state in blood, and Coulomb's law of the particulate component of the electron.

This historic background shows that Burr's and Northrop's *Electro-Dynamic Theory of Life* was the logical and inevitable application to biology of mathematical reasoning stretching back through the centuries. It was, in fact, more obvious than novel.

But it often takes genius to perceive the obvious.

Chapter Two

A Theory Emerges

1

The Electro-Dynamic Theory of Life was the offspring of the happy marriage of two brilliant minds that richly complemented one another and, as we have seen, their epoch-making discovery had an ancient and honorable ancestry.

Dr. Filmer S. C. Northrop had made a long and profound study of mathematical and philosophic concepts which were to form the solid foundation of the *Theory*. Dr. Harold Saxton Burr contributed a deep knowledge of neurology and of experimental techniques which, in the years following the publication of the *Theory* have demonstrated its validity in all forms of life to which it has been applied.

It is not only interesting but also important to describe some of the background of these two men. This will show that the *Theory* had an impeccable philosophic foundation. It will also show how it came about that the *Theory* was validated in a relatively short period of time by tireless and dedicated experiments.

Though both men must share equal credit for the origin of the *Theory*, Burr spent many years on its experimental verification and is thus better known for his part in the discovery.

In many ways Burr was quite unlike the brilliant scientist of popular imagination. Certainly, he was completely dedicated to his self-imposed task of "putting questions to nature and trying to get the answers," as he used to say, and in this task he stinted neither time nor energy. But he was much more than the scientist so often portrayed by fiction writers.

He was a scholar and a gentleman, not interested in personal aggrandizement and, for that reason, not too successful in making his work better known. He was so modest, in fact, that when The Honorable Edward W. Russell edited his definitive work, *Blueprint for Immortality* (American title: *The Fields of Life*), Burr suggested that Russell should publish the book as his own—an offer which, of course, was refused.

Intellectual integrity was the keynote of his character. He would neither claim nor publish anything until he was certain that he had sufficient experimental evidence. With his high standards of integrity, he could not tolerate the lack of it in others and was not afraid to express his opinion of dubious conduct if the need arose, which did not enhance his popularity with some of his colleagues. He kept himself aloof from the petty jealousies and squabbles that often infect academia and, in consequence, was sometimes unaware of efforts by lesser men to minimize the importance of his work.

His interests extended far beyond his own field. Though rigid in his own standards of accuracy, as a broadminded philosopher he was always open to new ideas and tolerant of the opinions of others. But he would not commit himself to a definite opinion about some new concept unless he could adduce supporting and, preferably, experimental evidence. For that reason, those who knew him perceived that he knew and privately believed much more than he would admit publicly.

He was a warm, understanding human being with a keen sense of humor. I have the happiest memories of the cheerful hospitality of Burr and his charming wife in what he called "the taproom" of

*A colored print of "the taproom," built circa 1684, with Burr sitting before the fireplace, appears in Taylor B. Lewis Jr.'s and Joanne Young's *Christmas in New England*, published in 1972 by Holt, Rinehart and Winston, p.9. The picture appears in reverse. The structure, originally a general store, was moved and attached to the original 1700 wing.

his historic old house at Lyme, Connecticut, one wing of which had been built by his family in 1700.*

A religious man, he was a conscientious supporter of his church and was even prepared to dress up as a swami and tell fortunes at the annual church fair—an unusual concession for a great scientist!

Learning of this, two friends lunching with Burr asked if he would tell their fortunes if they made a donation to church funds. Burr laughingly agreed and examined their palms across the luncheon table. They later reported to me that he was embarrassingly accurate in his character analysis. In reply to their questions, Burr emphatically denied having any psychic ability, explaining that the lines in the hand were all part of nature's organization and could be read by anyone who took the trouble to study the subject.

This episode illustrates how open Burr was to ideas apart from his own profession. It was because he had an inquiring mind, always hospitable to the unfamiliar. He was not afraid to question and re-examine some of the accepted tenets of biology.

He never made the mistake, too common among academics, of thinking that he had nothing more to learn. On the contrary, he always felt that nature had much to teach him if he could only ask the right questions.

That was the secret of his success.

2

Burr's first researches were in experimental neuroembryology, for which he used salamanders. He published two papers on the subject as far back as 1916. These were the first of the ninety-three papers he published in distinguished journals during the course of his life. Thus, he fully met the current academic requirement of "publish or perish."

This raises the interesting question of how much effect publication really has and whether the compelling urge to publish at all costs may not be self-defeating. So many papers pour out every year from the universities and laboratories that both journals and their readers tend to become surfeited. Too often papers are read only by a handful of specialists in a restricted field. If they suggest some new ideas unpalatable to the specialists, they are likely to be ignored.

That certainly happened in the case of Burr. Despite his distinguished post at Yale and despite the prestige of the journals in which his papers were published, few paid much attention and still fewer realized the importance of his work. Even an excellent photographic essay on his work, published in the August 14, 1944, issue of *Life* magazine with its vast circulation, seems to have aroused no attention in medical and scientific circles.

It did, however, have one useful consequence. It alerted the interest of the English writer, The Honorable Edward W. C. Russell, who later drew attention to the importance of Burr's work by editing his book which was published on both sides of the Atlantic and in three languages. It first appeared in Great Britain in 1972 and then in paperback in the United States in 1973.

Only two years before Burr's death in 1973, the importance of his work began to be appreciated. But this was not the result of the ninety-three papers and four books Burr had published.

Burr's discoveries encountered the usual resistance to new ideas, of which history has many examples. Philosopher that he was, Burr himself used to say that it would take at least thirty-five years before *The Electro-Dynamic Theory of Life* was accepted.

In the early 1930s, while studying the reorganization of the developing nervous system in salamanders, Burr noted certain phenomena which he felt could be explained in terms of electrodynamic or electromagnetic field forces. These observations were published in

1932 in two papers concerning the previously mentioned olfactory nerve transplant and its aberrant behavior in wandering off and connecting to an entirely strange portion of the nervous system. The first paper showed that specific function plays a negligible role in influencing the growth and differentiation of cerebral hemispheres. The development of these seems to be conditioned by the *positions* of nuclear masses in an electrodynamic field. The masses then influence ingrowing neurons which, in turn, stimulate internal organization. The hemispheres remain dormant until the experiential life of the individual adds activity to the pattern of structure. In short, structure precedes function. The electrodynamic field is primary, determining the pattern or organization of any growing system and hence, the behavior, development and orientation of its parts.

During the summer and fall of 1924, Burr had studied with C. U. Ariens Kappers in Amsterdam and his first 1932 paper confirmed Kapper's discovery that the growth and orientation of nerve fibers and the nervous system were conditioned by galvanic or electric factors. Burr felt, however, that his electrodynamic theory gave a more valid explanation of the position and location of the nuclear masses. His second paper elaborated and further confirmed his earlier findings. Thus, living systems at last began to be brought into harmony with field physics.

3

By a fortunate coincidence, during this period Burr's later associate, Northrop, in his Harvard graduate work, had been studying the same problem as Burr. Northrop's Ph.D. thesis, written under the guidance of L. J. Henderson, the Gibbsian physiologic chemist of the Harvard Medical School, and William Ernest Hocking in the Harvard Philosophy Department, was titled: "The Problem of

Organization in Biology."

It was natural that Burr and Northrop should join forces when Northrop was called to the Yale Philosophy Department in 1923 to teach mathematical logic and the history-philosophy of mathematical-physical as well as biologic science. Burr's and Northrop's respective talents complemented one another in an essential way. This was one of the happiest coincidences in the history of science. At the time when Burr's experiments were steering him from theories of a "physiologic gradient" to a measurable electrodynamic theory of biologic organization, Northrop was on the same track.

Northrop's study of the problem, in the light of Henderson's blood nomogram, was rewarded with a Sheldon Traveling Fellowship (1922-1923) in connection with his Ph.D. thesis (1924). From June to August 1922 at the University of Freiburg, he perfected his German and studied under Husserl, then Europe's foremost philosopher, who introduced "phenomenology." The noted embryologist, Hans Spemann, was Professor of Zoology at Freiburg.

From October 1922 to June 1923, at Henderson's instigation, Northrop enrolled not only as a Graduate Research Fellow at Trinity College, Cambridge,* under J. M. E. McTaggart's direction in philosophy, but also at the Imperial College of Science and Technology, University of London, where he went weekly to study, under Alfred North Whitehead's supervision, the methods and assumptions of contemporary physics. He was especially interested in both particle physics and Maxwellian-Einsteinian field physics, each division considered indispensable and irreducible.

Northrop's studies included the differences between Whitehead's and Einstein's relativity theories. In London, he attended Sir Ernest Rutherford's and Sir Arthur Eddington's lectures on Einsteinian math-physics.

These advanced, comprehensive studies and Henderson's

*At that time, Trinity College contained the largest assemblage of Nobel Laureates in the world.

nomogram inspired Northrop to formulate The Macroscopic Atomic Theory in 1922. This was initially published in 1928—a year before Einstein's 1929 Unitary Field Theory. The latter offered further evidence for Northrop's theory because it postulated the spatial, the gravitational and the electromagnetic fields as one aspect of a single continuum.

Northrop's Macroscopic Atomic Theory paved the way for his later collaboration with Burr. His theory presented an enormous amount of concrete evidence for the view that the Universe can be characterized by an electrodynamic field which gives unity to the whole and imposes position and direction of movement on all describable entities. In turn, the entities, or particles, determine and condition the field.

The prevailing scientific view in biology and medicine was rather that the whole—or field—is merely an aggregate of its parts and processes, rather than a causal effect in itself. Northrop acknowledged that though life is a mechanical-physico-chemical system calling for a kinetic atomic theory, it also involves a type of physico-chemical stability which cannot be conditioned solely by traditional atomic theory with its emphasis on collections of microscopic particles in motion, physico-chemical interaction, entities rather than organization, discontinuity rather than continuity and upon local systems rather than upon their status in the total field of nature as a whole. Furthermore, recent findings in wave mechanics and quantum theory at that time reduced chemical atoms to electrons and protons, implying that more fundamental electrodynamic factors underlie life.

In short, atomic physics had to be supplemented with field physics. Northrop explained that the importance of his Macroscopic Atomic Theory lay in the fact that its very existence as a possible theory demonstrated that the two differing traditional and modern scientific viewpoints could be combined without contradiction, for it made possible an aggregate of many particles, or entities, within a single system in which there was a reciprocal interaction between field and particle. Thus, for example, the fate of any group of cells is determined not only by a certain genetic constitution but by a certain cellular environment and a certain position in the electrodynamic field as well.

This work was an important influence on Northrop's part in originating with Burr an electrodynamic theory which covered not only the dynamics of development but also the pattern of organization of unitary biologic systems. In doing so, they postulated that fundamental universal law operates in living and nonliving matter alike, the difference between them to be found in more complex fields and more complex molecular structure. Thus, the organization of living systems was placed on the same objective and physical basis as the analysis of matter in the physical world.

Northrop's Macroscopic Atomic Theory was first published in the *Journal of Philosophy*, August 16, 1928, and in the Physics Section of the *Proceedings of the National Academy of Sciences, U.S.* in January 1930. He elaborated it in *Science and First Principles* in 1931. His theory provided the key thesis of that book.

4

Northrop reinforced the foundations of the 1935 Burr-Northrop paper through his frequent European trips and by his study of all classic electrodynamic Maxwell and Einstein books, papers and equations. Convinced that Einstein's reasoning was correct, Northrop arranged a meeting with him at the University of Berlin on June 28, 1927, which was before most Americans had heard of his existence.

At their initial meeting in Berlin and again just before his death in 1955, Einstein indicated that the covariant chronogeometric tensor of his 1916 General Theory of Relativity permits two alternative solutions: (1) the generally accepted one, which assumes in a finite physical universe the time flow to be constant, in which case the diameter of the finite physical universe is, with respect to the Doppler effect from distant nebulae, an expanding variable and (2) the other alternative of Northrop's theory which keeps the three dimensional physical diameter constant and entails a decreasing time flow for these stellar Doppler effect phenomena.

Both Burr and Northrop were exceptionally well prepared for their collaboration on the *The Electro-Dynamic Theory of Life*. In advancing this, they proposed that no specific scientific subject matter is trustworthy unless its proponents have discovered relevant and appropriate mathematics and mathematical logic to support it. They advanced the *Theory* only as a partial answer to the biologic problem of organization and design.

With their feet firmly planted on the findings of Faraday, Maxwell, Einstein, Gibbs and also on the transformations of Larmor and Lorentz, they felt justified in advancing the *Theory* before they had any experimental biologic evidence. Their extensive knowledge of relativity physics, biology and the history of science provided enough evidence for their assertion that the pattern, organization, behavior and continuity of a living system is determined by a complex electrodynamic field interacting with its atomic physico-chemical components.

All that Burr and Northrop did was to bring together previously observed data by a consistent theory which permitted new testable predictions.

Uninformed critics suggested that Burr was only measuring skin potentials. Aside from the lack of skin in slime molds, corn and cotton seeds, the inner growing layers of trees, etc., Burr's critics did not bother to find out that with suitably sensitive instruments it is possible to measure such basic voltage gradients with the electrodes a short distance *away* from the surface of the tested object under certain conditions. These facts, and the experiment with the salamander, effectively dispose of such criticisms.

Criticism of anything novel in any field often tends to be emotional rather than rational. Frequently, the emotional level almost reaches religious intensity as Burr learned. That Planck learned the same thing is reflected by his quote in the opening chapter of this book and why, all too often, the older generation cannot be made "to see the light."

Since the *Theory* was first proposed in 1935, it has been experimentally validated and no critic has ever successfully challenged either the *Theory* or Burr's experiments.

Chapter Three

SIX QUESTIONS TO NATURE

1

A theory which defines biologic phenomena in terms of energy differs from Bergson's *élan vital,* Driesch's entelechy and mechanical or chemical tropisms because it is amenable to *objective, quantitative, reproducible measurements* of the energy of living forms.

How does a living form differ from, say, a stone? Usually because it has a more complex structure and can exchange energy with its environment. "Usually" is used advisedly because such forms as viruses sometimes behave like living forms and sometimes like isolated protein molecules which do not, as far as is known, interchange any energy.

The proposition that *living systems in their totality comprise continuous electric fields* can be verified by putting, as Burr did, the following questions to nature:

1. *Do reproducible, relatively steadystate standing potential differences exist in every form of life?*

2. *Do these reproducible potential differences exhibit any configurations?*

3. *Does the pattern of the standing potential differences so measured correlate with the pattern of the organic form?*

4. *Can these configured potential differences be, in any sense of the word, measurable attributes of an electrodynamic (electromagnetic or quasielectrostatic) field?*

5. *Is such a field a consequence of the living process or is it, as the basic assumptions would require, a primary attribute of protoplasm*

capable of organizing its structure and activities?

6. *Can the effect of any cosmic forces on living systems be measured?*

It is relatively simple to "put these questions to nature," but difficult to get the answers. Considerable imagination was required to devise experiments to induce nature to reply.

New techniques had to be invented which required instruments—novel for those days—which could measure minute potential differences with negligible disturbance to the system being measured.

Many forms of living organisms had to be measured, and their sizes and variety often presented further difficulties. Also, since direct contact of metal electrodes with organisms produces unwanted artifacts, it was necessary to design electrodes, as described previously, to operate in salt solution or salt paste in approximate ionic equilibrium with that of the system being measured. The electrodes were originally embedded in lucite holders which minimized disturbance to the saline solution and reduced temperature gradients between the two electrodes to zero.

An additional problem was that no experiments had ever been done to determine the best points at which to measure potential differences and these had to be found by trial and error. In general, the electrode that was connected to the cold (reference or ground) lead of the amplifier was usually put somewhere on the living system at some distance from the area which was under investigation. The so-called hot (exploratory or grid) electrode was then placed as close as possible to the area under investigation.

Today, details of the Burr-Lane-Nims instruments are only of historic interest as a remarkable technical achievement for those days. Since then, the explosive advances of the electronic arts and the development of transistors have made commercial instruments more readily available. However, it is still essential to use special silver-silver chloride electrodes basically as they were made and used then.

When all this special apparatus had finally become operational, Northrop's great excitement was reflected in his words:

> ...what theory foretold, the electrodes found...living as well as nonliving things are electrodynamic systems.

2

1. Do reproducible, relatively steadystate standing potential differences exist in every form of life?

Burr's electrodes and micro- and millivoltmeters verified in a few years that steadystate potential differences exist in reproducible form in *all* the forms of life he tested and at all possible points on the organism. Though not invariant, these voltage gradients persist with a predictable constancy through the complex flux of chemical reactions which accompany growth and the living process.

2. Do these reproducible potential differences exhibit any configurations?

Measured fields of species, strains and individuals were found to have definite characteristic patterns according to the species.

For example, it was found that different potential patterns occur in two apparently identical, though distinct, strains of mice. One strain tended to produce malignancy in a high percentage of offspring while the other had a low percentage of neoplastic growth.

Even the right and left sides of living systems often differ in polarity. Burr soon found that the right half of the body may be of one polarity and the left may be of the other polarity in many of the individuals tested, whether or not they were right-handed or left-handed. However, later studies showed individual variations associated with age, sex and electrocyclic patterns.

3. Does the pattern of the standing potential differences so measured correlate with the pattern of the organic form? For example, do voltage gradients change with growth?

Voltage gradients of such forms as chick embryos, salamanders and plant roots (Obelia geniculata) progressively increase in magnitude—an increase which corresponds with the rate of cell division. With cell division onset, voltage fluctuations are superimposed on a steady potential gradient. For example, throughout blastulation and morulation stages in the salamander, potentials rise at an increasing rate until the free-swimming larval stage. At the end of the first third of the animal's life, these voltages reach a peak, level off during the middle third and decline during senescence (Burr and Hovland).

Similarly, studies of other forms of life, such as chickens, mice, plants and trees, showfluctuating increments in the first third of life which become relatively stable during the middle third and decline during the last. Unstable voltage increases during early life were also found in the initial differentiation of corn and cotton seeds which reflect the biologic activity of growth.

Nowhere, however, is this more dramatically represented than in the life cycle of the Obelia hydranth (Burr and Hammett). There exists a perfect correspondence between the direction of the voltage gradients and the progress of the life cycle. The voltage gradients correspond with all biologic fluctuations. They reflect the anabolic hydroplasmic streaming toward the growing animals and also the irreversible hydroplasmic streaming away from the senile, disintegrating creatures when there are rapid drops in potential differences. As regression continues, the potential drops level off until suddenly the polarity reverses.

The distal surface which had been negative to the base of the hydrotheca now becomes over 200 mv positive to it. Moreover, when dissolution is almost over, there is a sudden voltage shift to neutral which heralds the resting stage preparatory to the production of a new animal.

These experiments not only indicated voltage changes which correspond with the growth and change of the structure but also that senile dissolution was accompanied by the shrinkage and dissolution of protoplasm from within—and, therefore, could readily be detected by the accompanying potential shifts.

4. Can these configured potential differences be, in any sense of the word, measurable attributes of an electrodynamic (electromagnetic or quasielectrostatic) field?

It did not take many experiments to obtain a positive answer to this question. It was soon obvious that the measurements could only be of an electrodynamic (electromagnetic or quasielectrostatic) field. For example, as mentioned above, it was found that measurements could be made with the electrodes separated from, and out of contact with, the surface of the living form. Further, in excised frog sciatic nerves, Mauro and Burr have observed that propagated impulses initiated by electric stimuli can be readily detected in the surrounding air without directly contacting the axis-cylinders. The recorded values parallel mathematically predicted curves within narrow margins. The experiment with the salamander confirmed the same thing through a saline medium.

Likewise, it was shown that ovulation could be detected from potential difference measurements of injury-free, hangnail-free fingertips. As no nerve connections exist between ovaries and fingertips, a field must be present to transmit activities in one part of the body to other points distal to it.

5. Is such a field a consequence of the living process or is it, as the basic assumptions would require, a primary attribute of protoplasm capable of organizing its structures and activities?

Measurements of the field of the female soon made it clear that the field *is* a primary prerequisite of life, capable of organizing its structures and activities. These measurements showed that variations in field measurements *preceded* physical events. Anything that precedes an event cannot be its consequence, but must have some part in organizing it.

Burr's earlier experiments with the salamander showed that—contrary to prevailing theory—the pattern of organization of the developing nervous system was laid down before the animal made any functional demands.

6. *Can the effect of any cosmic forces on living systems be measured?*

There exist empiric correlates of lunar phases with many phenomena such as birth rates, psychiatric patient perturbations and increased incidence of crime.

As has already been noted, cosmic forces have measurable effects on the fields of trees, correlating with diurnal, lunar, seasonal and annual cycles, the annual variations correlating with the sunspot cycle. I later discovered the same cycles in human subjects.

These brief answers to Burr's fundamental questions will be amplified and clarified by detailed descriptions of other important experiments.

3

Do the fields of males and females have any distinct characteristics?

If the voltage gradients are as basic as the *Theory* stipulates, we would expect a difference between the voltage output of males and females. It was no surprise to Burr, therefore, to find that the voltage differences between the corresponding right and left fingers of women varied with their menstrual cycles. For some 24-48 hours before the egg was released, field measurements showed marked variations—another example of the fact that changes in the field often precede a physical event. At the time the egg was released, there was a very large spike in the EMF.

When measurements were made on female rabbits, a rhesus monkey and an albino rat, sharp rises at ovulation were also detected.

These observations suggested laparotomies (abdominal operations) and microscopic examination during voltage gradient peaks. A required laparotomy for one human subject was timed during her measured voltage gradient peaks and confirmed the release of the egg at the peak voltage. The measurements were made with the hot (exploratory) electrode on the wall of the vagina in the vicinity of the cervix and the cold (reference) electrode on the central abdominal wall, while a combined millivoltmeter and General Electric photoelectric recorder obtained continuous tracings.

This laparotomy was the first time known to me that the event of human ovulation was measured electronically and a prediction confirmed.

In later studies, Burr simplified and improved his measurement by placing the ground or reference electrode on the ankle and the other on the cervix uteri. Under these conditions it was found that at least once in the majority of menstrual cycles, the cervix, which is usually positive to the ankle, switches polarity and becomes negative for between 24-48 hours. This polar reversal is not usually demonstrated when right and left finger potential differences are measured. These usually show slow, pronounced rhythmic oscillations in close sequence, the spikes usually being of either plus or minus polarity.

In two instances, artificial insemination resorted to at the time of the negative shift resulted in pregnancy. Forty-eight hours after the negative shift, vaginal smears showed characteristic changes and pregnandiol in the urine indicated that ovulation had occurred. Interestingly, this also occurred when two supposedly sterile individuals showed typical ovulatory spikes. On the other hand, no potential peaks or spikes could be found on women who did not ovulate, on fertile women after pregnancy or after menopause.

These experiments led to a most important finding. Burr's discovery of voltage variations in ovulation (in collaboration with and confirmed by Barton, Boling, Hill, Allen, Musselman, Kelley, Langman and Ravitz) made the following facts clear: in addition to ovulating during the middle of their menstrual cycles, many women ovulate at other times, including the menstrual period itself, though menstrual ovulation is rare. As Burr has written:

> Like brain waves and heart waves, electrometric changes occur during ovulation and...may take place at any time in the menstrual cycle, although, in the majority of women studied, the ovulation record showed the mid-cycle peak. It is equally clear that there is no necessary relationship between ovulation and menstruation, for either may exist without the other; ovulation may occur without menstruation and menses without ovulation.

These findings explain why the "rhythm method" of birth control is unreliable. Electrometric measurements are a more reliable guide to ovulation. Such measurements, which vary with the individual, are easy to make with modern instruments. As Burr found early in his work, they can be used either to avoid pregnancy or to achieve it. In fact, by electrometric measurement of ovulation, Burr enabled a patient to have a much-longed-for child.

As electrometric determinations of ovulation can be made between the fingers, they involve no intrusion into the body.

When these important findings are generally realized and

accepted and when the necessary instruments are available, family planning will be possible with much greater ease.

4

It has long been known that the time taken for wounds to heal varies with the individual. Burr, Harvey and Taffel demonstrated in various living forms that the healing of wounds is reflected by changes in the voltage gradients of the field. It is, therefore, possible to measure the progress of healing in the patient, even if the wound cannot be inspected. They also found that the magnitude of the abnormal voltages reflects the extent of the damage.

When this practical application of the *Theory* is in general use, it will be possible to determine the degree of wound healing even beneath the skin.

5

Since wounds show corresponding voltage changes, we would expect to find the same thing when peripheral nerves are injured. Burr found that this is so. There are profound potential changes when there is loss of function—from whatever cause—but before function is restored (or the nerve regenerated), the electric pattern returns to optimal level prior to any signs of clinical improvement.

This quantitative test of peripheral nerve function was developed by Grenell and Burr first on rabbits and then on war-injured personnel at the Oak Knoll Naval Hospital, Oakland, California, and at the U.S. Naval Hospital, St. Albans, New York.

In rabbits, voltage gradients were plotted prior to nerve injury or nerve block. After this, 2% procaine or procaine-suprarenin (1:20,000 and 1:50,000) was injected into the nerve being investigated. Potentials were also measured prior to and following interruption of the nerve pathway.

The hot (exploratory) electrode was placed on the area innervated and the cold (reference) electrode was placed on the upper thigh in rabbits and on the ear lobe in human patients.

Voltage gradients obtained in this way were controlled by potential measurements on the undisturbed limb, by voltage determinations of the same places on organisms which had been injected with isotonic saline solution and by procaine infiltrations into nerves which had been crushed some weeks before. Peripheral nerve response was also studied in humans who had undergone bilateral or unilateral operations on the sympathetic nervous system.

In both rabbit and human, as long as the peripheral nerve was intact, the further electrode always read negative to the nearer one. Crushing or severing the sciatic nerve in rabbits produced a marked voltage shift to the positive, despite central depression by anesthesia, comparable to the temporary procaine block. In the latter case, voltages would return to optimal levels within two hours, in contrast to the lack of potential shift following saline injections. Procaine injections into rabbit sciatic nerves which had been crushed weeks before, or into paralyzed human ulnar nerves failed to produce any voltage shifts until regeneration was complete.

By contrast, following procaine block of intact peripheral nerves, human subjects showed even more pronounced potential shifts than the rabbits—as much as 55 mv—which was partly due to their unanesthetized state. In no case were there any signs of sensory or motor return until the potential gradients had reverted to at least 50% of their pre-injection or pre-traumatic level. In cases of repaired ulnar nerves where the potential differences between the two electrodes were less negative than might have been expected, the voltage gradients correlated with neurologic tests which showed that regeneration was not yet complete.

In even a bilateral preganglionic sympathectomy for Raynaud's disease, intact ulnar nerves continued to show the usual plus voltage shift following procaine block, though in the case of a unilateral sympathectomy, the intact peripheral nerve on the operated side showed a slower positive increase to that of the intact side.

To date, voltage gradients have not been plotted in relation to postganglionic sympathectomies. However, the use of instruments designed to measure pure voltage gradients independent of resistance and current flow, together with the fact that rapid shutting off and releasing blood to the forearm through a blood-pressure cuff fails to produce potential changes, suggest that the described voltage alterations cannot be attributed to vascular changes.

Though, obviously, there is plenty of scope for further research on the effects of nerve damage on voltage gradients, Burr's meticulous research already shows that here is a useful tool for neurosurgeons.

Chapter Four

The Essential Organization

Decades have passed since the war on cancer was first declared, yet at the close of the Twentieth Century, it is still among the leading reasons for death in the United States.

Scientists have looked to many possible causes for the dread disease and have found links to such factors as genetic inheritance, nutritional deficiencies, drugs, radiation and tobacco. Research shows that pesticides in food and soil, chemicals used for water treatment and toxins in the air we breathe are all carcinogenic.

We are warned to avoid unnecessary x-rays, to exercise, eat fruits and cruciferous vegetables and to wash them thoroughly before eating, filter our drinking water, wear sunscreen for even the shortest excursions outside and to stop smoking.

These dramatic warnings are all valid but obviously none of them has provided any cure for cancer. There seems to be general agreement that the best way to stay well is through prevention and that the best hope for recovery is early detection. But even here, traditional screening tools are unable to catch certain fast growing and aggressive cancers in time. This is where field measurements can be valuable and helpful because abnormalities in the field can give warning of impending malignancy before there are any overt symptoms.

It has been decades since Burr and his colleagues made and published these important discoveries. But in spite of all the millions spent on cancer research and of all the talk about "making war on cancer," few, if any, of those engaged in cancer research seem to have availed themselves of this extraordinary information or to have followed up Burr's work.

Essentially, cancer is the result of disorganization of some of the physiologic processes of the body. Instead of developing normally, certain groups of cells "go wild" and proliferate erratically. Usually this disorganization is confined to one part of the body. But certain forms of cancer can metastasize and rapidly spread this disorganization throughout the body.

Since the field organizes the physical form, disorganization in the latter indicates that there is something wrong with the organizing field. Or to put it another way, instead of obeying the regulations of the field, some cells escape from this control and form new growths "on their own," so to speak.

Though aberrant growths are usually localized except, say, in leukemia and metastasis, this disorganization affects the entire field, and aberrant voltage gradients can be detected by applying electrodes remote from the area affected.

This is only to be expected because voltage gradients change with cell multiplication, as we have seen in cases of growth, wound healing and nerve regeneration. It is natural, therefore, to predict that neoplastic growth would be associated with atypical alterations in field pattern measurements.

In short, cancer represents a breakdown of organizing forces.

Until the "generals" of the armies engaged in the "war on cancer" realize this fact, they are likely to be as ineffective as military commanders without a proper intelligence system. A study of the variations in the organizing field is as essential in cancer research as is a knowledge of the enemy's plans in successful military operations, because only a study of the field can give advance warning of the invasion of cancer.

2

In mice, Burr, G. M. Smith and L. C. Strong established that there were differences in field measurements between animals with spontaneous breast cancer, those with malignancies produced by carcinogens (e.g., methyl colanthrene-induced sarcomas) and those with atypical transplanted growths.

Inflammation, necrosis and ulceration change field patterns and complicate analysis. In spite of this, however, malignancy superimposes its own characteristic variations which can partially be isolated by producing nonmalignant ulcerations with such an agent as benzene.

In mice, there are vivid electric distinctions between embryonic and both rapid- and slow-growing neoplastic tissues. The rapidly growing tumors produce the most intense voltage gradients which develop more quickly than the lower voltages associated with late starting and sluggish implants.

Relatively benign tumor masses, however, show potential curves which parallel those of the rapidly growing neoplasms and which even reach their maxima at about the same time. On the other hand, fetal tissues get off to a prompt start, reach their maxima ahead of the others and then decrease to zero. This is followed by polar reversals and a return to zero.

These potential plots are curiously similar to those associated with wound healing, particularly in their sequence in time. Moreover, potential decreases correspond with the onset of necrosis in the neoplastic groups and with the retrogression of embryonic tissues in the fetal groups. They also correspond with the similar voltage shifts which occur when senescent organisms start to break down.

In mice, abnormal growth is usually electronegative to tissue which is not involved. This is best demonstrated by plotting maximal potential—measuring potential differences between the peripheral disease area and a healthy reference point in a body cavity, such as the mouth. This is better than plotting the lower potential gradients between two surface areas.

3

These findings of the relationship between malignancy and voltage variations encouraged Burr to examine the same phenomenon in women. With the collaboration of Louis Langman, M.D., Burr studied the potentials associated with malignancy in the generative tracts of more than 900 women in the Gynecological Department of Bellevue Hospital in New York City. Data from 860 patients were analyzed statistically. On the basis of complete physical examinations and biopsies, 123 were judged to be suffering from malignant growths. Of these, 118 had shown negative readings, the fornix being negative to the lower abdominal wall used as a reference point. The remaining five patients in this group showed positive posterior fornix voltage gradients. Statistically, this gave a chi-square value of 318.5, the significant number being 3.842.

When all the subjects were subdivided into age groups 21- 40 and 40-60, the chi-square calculation for the younger group became 131.2, that for the older group, 80.6. In at least one case where the cervix was negative, the pathologic report was equivocal, though a second biopsy confirmed a diagnosis of cancer.

It may be of significance to note that treatment of genito urinary malignancy, either by radium or x-ray, has not affected the voltage gradients in any way. On the other hand, of the 737 malignancy-free patients, 611 showed electropositive fornix readings; 126, or approximately 18%, demonstrated negative polar reversals.

In the younger age bracket, about one-third of the negative fornix readings could be accounted for by ovulation. Moreover, a variety of benign miscellaneous conditions was found in another third, including uterine pregnancy, recent abortions, pelvic inflammatory disease and so on. Still, at least 6% showed electronegativity in the absence of any demonstrable disease, ovulation or pregnancy, particularly among the older post-menopausal age group, in which this finding paralleled the increased incidence of malignancy.

It follows that the presence of negative potentials in the genitourinary tract in even a small proportion of cases where there is no demonstrable pathology, raises the question of whether this finding may have predictive value. Under appropriate circumstances at some future time, will patients with such polarities develop cancer? This is something, of course, which voltage readings cannot predict with certainty. But they *can* indicate a disorganization of the field, which may result in malignancy even if symptoms are not visible. This, of course, can be of great value to the physician. It alerts him and gives time to take corrective measures before the malignancy gets out of hand.

It should be emphasized that the voltage correlates of local pathology, such as malignancy in the genito urinary tract, appear to be superimposed on the entire organization and can be detected by measurements remote from the affected area.

4

We can now consider a more detailed answer to the third question which Burr posed to nature:

Does the pattern of the standing potential differences so measured correlate with the pattern of the organic form?

As electrometric observations of various life forms throughout the plant and animal kingdoms reveal characteristic voltages which correspond with development and cell division, it follows that there must be a corresponding relationship between voltage gradients and form. This can be illustrated by the examination of plant embryos.

Since Sinnott had already established a basis for examining such relations in cucurbit plant embryos which have forms simpler than those of animals, Burr and Sinnott chose for examination four inbred races of Cucurbita pepo (the common pumpkin). They have elongated yellow fruits (straightneck squash), round white plants, flat white scallop gourds and hookneck gourds.

Through voltage measurements taken along both axial and equatorial diameters, they discovered that although the magnitude of the voltage gradient did not seem to depend on the size of the embryo, the ratio of the two dimensions corresponded with the ratios of field differences in length and width—an indication that voltage gradients correlate with form.

Additional evidence of this correlation was afforded by similar experiments with irregular and asymmetric fruits. For example, one flat fruit, much longer in one diameter than in the other, confirmed its unusual shape electrically by yielding corresponding differences between voltages read on the two diameters. Also, when electrodes were placed on the tips of the blunt teeth of the scallops surrounding the equator of the flat fruits, the voltage gradients differed markedly from those recorded on the sinus between them.

During development, the voltage gradient along the larger diameter rises more steeply than the voltage along the smaller diameter. Thus throughout the development of the form, the ratios of length-to-width potentials increase in the elongated fruits, remain unchanged in round fruits and decrease in flat gourds, despite the fact that in all types of the fruit, the absolute voltage gradients (mv per mm) tend to decrease as the fruits grow larger.

5

These experiments on plant embryos suggested that the voltage gradient in plant seeds should also be studied in order to find out if these corresponded with the subsequent growth and development of the plant. This seemed important because so much work had been done on the genetics of seeds, particularly maize. So Burr attempted to explore this problem with the cooperation of W. W. Singleton of the Connecticut Agricultural Experimental Station, and later with O. E. Nelson Jr.

Over a three-year period, corn seeds were selected from six pure and ten hybrid strains which, from genetic studies, were known to possess very different properties. Among the inbred strains was a semi-dwarf, single-gene mutant.

This examination demanded exceptionally delicate experimental techniques, for which Burr and his colleagues had to devise minute silver-silver chloride electrodes of a kind never previously employed.

It was necessary to soak all maize seeds in tap water for thirteen to twenty-four hours before measurements could be taken. Voltage gradients were taken with the seed on a revolving stage which could rotate 180 degrees in relation to the exploratory and reference electrodes. By taking potentials at all possible surface points, it was soon discovered that the seeds exhibited a regular pattern of equipotential lines. The greatest potential difference occurred on the longitudinal axis between micropylar (flat) and germinal (apical) ends. The micropylar extremity was usually electronegative to the germinal end. Measurements across the other two dimensions, from side-to-side and from back-to-front, were smaller than those along the long axis.

During the experiment, two potentials were plotted for each seed and controlled by samples picked at random. The first, or prime potential, was obtained by touching the electrodes to the micropylar and germinal ends of the long axis and taking an immediate reading, for the initially unstable voltage tends to fall off rapidly from 30 to 120 seconds. It then becomes stable for two to five minutes, probably because ionic equilibrium between the seeds and the saline dielectric has been reached. A second reading was taken during this relatively quiescent period and designated the "equilibrium potential."

When the seed was subsequently planted, its prime potential had anticipated its kernel viability or quality, irrespective of any known genetic factors.

On the other hand, the equilibrium potential was not associated in any way with viability. It did show, however, a predictable correlation with the growth history in the field and with the genetic constitution of the kernel.

The high-potential seeds (seventeen to thirty mv) grew faster and taller and also produced a bigger yield of large-size seeds than did seeds in the intermediate group (six to twelve mv). The latter proved superior to the low-potential seeds (zero to four mv) and also to the single-gene mutant with a voltage 1/4 of its parents.

With seven out of nine entries, it was possible to separate high- and low-potential seeds by their growth rates early in the season. The remaining two entries were kept until the close of the season to compare their growth rates.

At every point in the growing season, however, the high-potential plants were taller, sturdier and leafier than those with intermediate or low voltages. Comparisons of potentials of inbred and hybrid lines demonstrate that between a hybrid and two inbreds, voltage gradients of the hybrid are typically larger than those of the inbred with smaller potentials and, in fact, may exceed the potential of either parents.

In every instance, the electrometric distinctions of the 1943 and 1944 F_2 generations were reflected in proportional voltage gradients in the 1945 and 1946 F_3 and F_4 stock. The high-, intermediate- and low-potential seeds produced high-, intermediate- and low-potential offspring; and when these were planted they could be compared with these electric characteristics. There was, however, an inexplicable finding (now somewhat less enigmatic in the light of later experiments with other forms of life). This was the considerable rise of potential in all F_3 and F_4 progeny by comparison with the F_2 seeds. At the time, it was thought that the F_2 stock might have embodied some superior growth factors. But what forces could have triggered the demonstration of superior qualities many months later? A clue to this is suggested in Chapter 5.

6

This discovery of the relationship in maize between the voltage gradients and genetic constitution and also with hybrid vigor suggested that the same thing might be found with cotton seeds.

In this case, however, the problem, commissioned by the Southern Regional Research Laboratory of the U.S.D.A., was rather different. It was to determine the effect of various chemical treatments on the voltage gradients of the seeds. As these seeds had various degrees of moisture content, it was not necessary to soak them before testing and only the "equilibrium potential" was tested.

Though the conditions of these experiments precluded an exhaustive analysis of viability and inherent vigor, cotton seeds exhibited patterns similar to those of maize. When planted on moistened filter paper in petri dishes and allowed to germinate in the dark, the highest potential seeds were the first to develop roots, followed by the intermediate and, finally, the lowest potential seeds.

Though only about 50% of all the seeds were viable, the evidence from these experiments suggests that the electrometric selection of the highest quality seeds could help to produce the healthiest, most vigorous and most productive plants.

7

To return to Burr's fourth question: *Can these configured potential differences be, in any sense of the word, measurable attributes of an electrodynamic (electromagnetic or quasielectrostatic) field?*

The *Theory* had predicted the existence of fields in all living forms and measurement of potential gradients had confirmed the prediction. To give added weight to these results, however, experiments were planned to demonstrate and measure potential gradients well outside the surfaces of the organisms. This was done by measuring field potentials propagated through fluid dielectrics.

An example of this was the experiment with the salamander. When this aquatic animal was rotated between two electrodes immersed in a saline solution, it caused a sine wave output similar to that of an AC generator. When the organism was removed from its fluid environment, or when a glass rod was rotated instead of the organism, no voltage differences were read. From this, it is evident that voltage differences in the dielectric could only be due to the presence of electric fields in the living creature.

This can also be demonstrated by inserting capillary electrodes into the gelatinous capsule of salamander embryos which are kept in constant rotation by actively beating cilia. With embryos, free-swimming larvae and younger animals, as we would expect, the potentials are lower than those of adult forms.

In humans, ovulation can be detected from finger potentials through surrounding salt solution without contact between the fingers and the electrodes. This is further evidence of a field phenomenon.

8

All this evidence suggested that the passage of a nerve impulse along a nerve fiber suspended in air would produce disturbances in the field strong enough to be detected at a distance from the nerve fiber itself. This proved to be correct. Using thirteen sciatic nerves of giant Louisiana bullfrogs, Burr and Mauro discovered that characteristic field disturbances could be recorded through the surrounding air 12mm from the nerve trunks despite the fact that air, unlike saline, is a poor conducting medium.

Comparing Lorente de Nó's trace of monophasic action-potential fields in an infinite volume conductor accompanying frog sciatic nerve impulses as a basis for the boundary conditions as the nerve surface, quasielectrostatic fields were predicted and plotted. The theoretic measurables closely approximated the recorded measurables to a distance of 4 cm from the nerves. Beyond this point, the field distortion of the probe interfered with accurate determinations.

Despite such preliminary difficulties, these experiments not only showed that there are electric fields in and about nerves which are disturbed when the nerves are excited, but also indicated the nature of these fields. At least in those experiments which dealt with nerves, it was clear that the simplest form of fields was being plotted: quasielectrostatic fields which behave in most ways like the electrostatic fields of the inorganic universe except that they change slowly in time.

Previous experiments had plotted the relatively stable fields of many forms of life. These experiments on nerves demonstrated that quasi-electrostatic fields are associated with biologic activity.

Chapter Five

Effects of Cosmic Forces

1

Can the effect of any cosmic forces on living systems be measured?

An affirmative answer to Burr's sixth question is not only of great scientific and medical importance, but also has potential philosophic and even political significance.

For if cosmic fields have a direct effect on the field of the human organism, this means that the human race is subject to the influence of great cyclic forces which it cannot evade or ignore. In other words, we are not quite as independent as we like to think, and it would be to our advantage to understand whatever relationship might exist between our health and well-being and nature's cosmic energies.

It is important to understand that if we are enveloped in and influenced by the great organizing fields of the universe, it also means that we are an integral part of that organization. As Burr wrote:

> The Universe in which we find ourselves and from which we cannot be separated is a place of Law and Order. It is not an accident, nor chaos. It is organized and maintained by an Electro-Dynamic Field capable of determining the position and movement of all charged particles.

Philosophically then, man, as a part of a highly organized Universe, is not an accident. We are not, as some still quaintly believe, the haphazard product of molecular copulation in some improbable, primeval, cosmic consommé.

If cosmic forces affect the human field, they are likely, as we shall see, to affect not only human health but also human behavior. Since cosmic forces operate in cycles, it is probable that there are times when the human race is especially subject not only to epidemics of disease but also to psychologic disturbance and unrest, making civil commotion and war more probable. If this could be established and the cycles plotted, it would have great political significance and usefulness.

An affirmative answer, therefore, to Burr's sixth question is of paramount importance.

Before we find it from Burr's experiments, it may be helpful to remind ourselves of some things which are already known apart from Burr's work.

It has long been realized that certain winds, such as the mistral and sirocco of the Mediterranean area, have profound effects on human behavior. It is even reported that a murder committed during the mistral can be excused.

In England at Easter, 1940, a friend of the editor, especially susceptible to winds of this kind, felt the effects of an unusually strong northeast wind of the mistral type. He learned later that this had been accompanied by changes in the earth's magnetic field of such intensity that some German magnetic mines exploded spontaneously.

With the known effects of the mistral or sirocco on human behavior, it is not too hard to imagine that changes in the cosmic fields, with which this planet is surrounded, could have similar and more powerful effects.

It has been noted that there are likely to be more births in maternity hospitals at certain lunar phases. Some psychiatric hospitals have observed that their patients tend to be more disturbed at these times.

It has long been known that cosmic forces have profound inorganic effects. Many years ago, John H. Nelson of the Radio Corporation of America discovered that certain alignments of the planets disrupted transatlantic shortwave radio communication by their effects on the ionosphere.

As this is written, there is much research into the probable effects of sunspots and solar storms on the climate and weather of this planet.

The human race, then, is rather like a shoal of fish swimming in an ocean with powerful currents. We exist in the vast ocean of cosmic fields, as ignorant as fish of the currents that affect us.

2

To obtain the answer to his sixth question directly from nature, Burr connected his instruments to trees, as they are alive, stay put and require minimal care. He realized, too, that to detect the effects of cosmic forces, voltage gradients would have to be continuously recorded over long periods, something thus far impossible to do with human subjects.

He started these experiments in 1942 and by 1943 continuous recordings had been made on elm, oak and maple trees in New Haven and Lyme, Connecticut. Silver-silver chloride electrodes surrounded by a bridge of saline paste were enclosed in weatherproof cases with one open side so that the paste could be in contact with the cambium layer of the tree. The bark was bandaged back over the electrodes, and the wires were run to nearby buildings in which the amplifiers and continuous recorders were housed. A pair of electrodes was set three to five feet apart, the lower one high enough from the ground to be immune from damage by animals.

This arrangement proved remarkably stable and the electrodes remained in place and functioned without trouble for many years.

Assuming that the Universe is organized by a vast electromagnetic field which gives unity to the whole and which imposes position and direction on all its entities, Burr reasoned that it should be possible to detect the effects of universal forces on living systems. Trees were most convenient for detecting these forces and if it was found that they affect trees, it was logical to assume that all living forms must be subject to their effects.

Over many years of continuous recording, several cycles of varying duration were recorded, from diurnal rhythms to lunar, seasonal and annual variations. Mathematical analyses of the recordings were made by Bliss, Wilpizeski and Markson. Neither voltage intensity, **E** nor polarity, **H** could in any way be correlated with daily temperatures, barometric pressure, amount of sunlight or the usual local weather conditions, including average wind velocity.

Though no correlates were found between local terrestrial and field variables, diurnal electromagnetic field variations were immediately spotted. During autumn, the trees showed their highest field intensities in late afternoon and their lowest in the morning. A diurnal shift of as much as 70 mv was sometimes observed.

It was soon discovered, however, that complete polar reversals were distributed throughout the year. For example, during the spring months, the trees showed their greatest field intensities in the early morning and the lowest in late afternoon. An alligator pear and a tomato plant in the laboratory revealed similar rhythms, though these were not in phase with the trees.

As D. T. MacDougal and F. W. Haasis had established the diurnal expansion and contraction of tree trunk diameters, continuous field measurements were supplemented by parallel dendographic measurements on a relatively young maple tree in Lyme during the summer of 1944.

As expected, dendographic studies showed that the tree diameter increased during the night and decreased during the day. From simultaneously plotted records of the standing potentials, or voltage gradients, it was immediately obvious that the diurnal electric rhythm was in opposite phase to the diameter rhythm, reaching a low in the early morning and a high late in the afternoon.

In the majority of the standing potential and dendographic records, this phase reversal was very striking. Occasionally, the EMF change was nearly in phase with the diameter change. Most remarkable, however, from September 10 to 12, there were profoundly wide swings in EMF potentials with no related changes in diameter. Diurnal variations in diameter may have diminished at the time because of the effects of dehydration during this very dry summer, but the fact remains that fluctuations in electric rhythms were as Burr put it, "astounding."

3

Occurring around the time of the great New England hurricane of September 14, 1944, the aforementioned event provided one of the most striking and significant studies of the thousands carried out by Burr. At that time, Burr's recording voltmeters were only monitoring two trees—an older maple at New Haven and a younger one at Lyme. As far as is known, these were the only two living systems in the world to be continuously monitored at that time.

From September 10 to 14, electrometrically precipitous plus polarity field variations occurred in both trees. For example, on September 10, the younger tree, which showed much wider field variations, shifted from an average maximum of *-50* mv at 6:00 a.m. to *+169* mv at noon, a range of 219 mv in six hours. Voltages then gradually decreased, reaching zero at 6:00 a.m. on September 11.

Again they rose precipitously in six hours to *+263* mv at noon.

By 4:00 a.m. on September 12, the voltage had decreased to zero but in the following eight hours reached *+388* mv by noon. This phenomenon recurred on the 13th and 14th, the plus potential increases exceeding any ever recorded for September.

During this enormous field flux, the second largest hurricane recorded in New England history struck on the evening of September 14. If these extraordinary potential shifts had been recorded in only one tree, little could have been made of them. But parallel changes occurred at the same time in both an old and a young tree forty miles apart. This suggested a causal relationship between the electric conditions of the troposphere, the hurricane and the fields of living systems. Unfortunately, owing to power failures and other mishaps, no Burr records are available for subsequent annual hurricanes.

It will be noticed that these violent voltage fluctuations started on September 10, four days before the actual hurricane. This suggests that living systems are sensitive to electromagnetic field changes which precede terrestrial phenomena.

This is supported by the well-known fact that certain living creatures seem to have some advance warning of an approaching storm and seek refuge or shelter. And it is reported that scientists have observed unusual behavior in animals in advance of earthquakes.

Be that as it may, Burr's long monitoring of field changes in trees is evidence of the potential impact of cosmic phenomena on all living creatures.

4

From time immemorial, men have sensed some relationship between the phases of the moon and living creatures. Down the centuries, for example, farmers have found empirically that certain crops grow better if they are planted at certain phases of the moon. Burr, therefore, was not surprised to find a relationship between the phases of the moon and the voltage gradients in the trees he was monitoring. For the first time in history known to this writer, his observations afforded a demonstrable, measurable basis for what man has so long realized.

As early as the summer of 1942 when the tree experiments were started, he observed potential shifts corresponding approximately with the periods of full and new moon, the greater variations occurring in the younger tree. These curious increments were regularly recorded in each succeeding year. Even during such drastic changes as occurred in the hurricane period, the voltage peaks were superimposed on slowly changing, relatively steady state straight-line configurations which displayed slow oscillations of 30 to 40 mv every 1 to 2 minutes. This phenomenon is not unlike the voltage variations seen at ovulation or during psychotic perturbations. In trees, such intense periodic oscillation usually persisted for about an hour and then disappeared, returning again during peaks of field intensity.

Prior to the 1944 hurricane, during the five-day period of full moon on September 2, daily field determinations on both trees averaged about 19 mv below their subsequently computed 1944 monthly means. The New Haven tree averaged about *0* to *+10* mv and the Lyme tree *-30* to *-20* mv.

The hurricane on the evening of the 14th occurred during a period of maximum positivity, less than three days prior to new moon on the 17th. During this phase their field variations averaged approximately 18 mv above the September 1944 monthly mean.

To show such voltage shifts statistically, the months of the winter and summer solstices and the spring and autumn equinoxes were grouped for 1943 and 1944. Then the mean diurnal voltage was charted for each of the four three-month periods and compared with the mean diurnal voltage during an arbitrary three-day period around new and full moon. Results of each of the four seasonal potential means were then subtracted from new and full moon means within each three-month period. These provided statistically significant correlated values for these lunations to the season.

In general, from November through January the upper electrode tends to be more positive at new moon than at full moon, though both lunar phases are positive to the mean for this interval. Throughout February, March and April the seasonal means which have been decreasing in positivity since mid-January, reach zero, change polarity and become increasingly negative.

This phenomenon is accompanied by parallel shifts in lunar means. Hence, the corrected means for new and full moon are still positive to the seasonal means. Due to a drop in voltage gradient, however, the corrected new moon mean appears slightly positive on the polarity spectrum while the corrected full moon mean is slightly negative to the zero line.

From May through July a polar reversal takes place. Greater field variations occur at full moon than at new moon, sandwiching the seasonal mean between. All three means, however, tend to be positive. The disparity between new and full moon rhythms is greatest in June.

Next, from August through October the lunar voltage pattern reverts to that associated with winter, the corrected new moon mean being positive to the corrected full moon mean. The seasonal mean starts out positive to both, shifts and becomes positive again to new and full moon by the end of August. However, at the beginning of September the gap between corrected lunar means closes, widens during the next thirty days and irons out by the end of October.

5

This statistical study did something more important than demonstrate field intensities and polarities during the phases of the moon and the seasons. It demonstrated the profound field changes which occur around the time the moon is in conjunction (moon interposed between sun and earth: new moon) and opposition (earth interposed between sun and moon: full moon). "Near" conjunction and opposition provides a more accurate description for such field shifts than exactly "at" conjunction and opposition, for as field maxima frequently occur before and/or after the precise lunar day, the form of the moon more often appears crescent or gibbous.

It would be wrong to suggest that the moon by itself affects terrestrial matter because neither the polarity nor the intensity of the voltage shifts remain constant and seem to depend on other factors, one of which correlates with the seasons. Complex calculations, too, failed to reveal any connection either between voltages and the lunar azimuth or moonlight intensity, as when moonlight is obscured by clouds. Incidentally, Bouger's assessment, over one hundred years ago, that moonlight at best is 1/300,000 of sunlight still holds true.

There exist interdependent shorter cycles within longer cycles. And despite the marked voltage swings near lunar conjunction and opposition, it is easier to discern three four-month seasonal cycles than the four three-month periods to which shorter term variations had been referred.

On an annual basis, the upper electrode becomes more positive to the lower steadily through the fall and reaches a maximum in December to January. After this, and throughout late winter and early spring, the voltage of the upper electrode decreases to zero and then becomes negative to the lower electrode, this negative polarity usually reaching a maximum between the end of April and July.

During the late spring and summer of 1944, the alligator pear showed similar voltage swings though this seasonal change tended to lag one month behind the maple tree in Lyme. Moreover, the tree fields become less positive before the sap begins to flow and reverse polarity before any buds appear. Throughout late summer the upper electrode again becomes more positive before the leaves fall or the sap flow slows down.

Though no terrestrial factors are known, the positive field maximum at the beginning of winter roughly coincides with the northern winter solstice on December 22 and with the perihelion (nearest point of earth to sun) on January 1. Similarly, the negative voltage maximum during late spring is close to the northern summer solstice on June 22 and not far from aphelion on July 2.

A secondary resurgence of plus polarity is found about the time of the autumn equinox of September 22, the hurricane season in northern latitudes. When these rhythms are plotted and compared over the years with the same reference points of winter solstices and moon phases, analogous though not identical curves are obtained. Yet even diurnal rhythms within different years seem to be more similar than different if linked to the same constants. Polarity shifts, also, are maximal near the vernal equinox on March 21 when the general voltage level is shifting into minus. Field variations in relation to any monthly mean become minimal in April.

Calculations show that tree voltage variations steadily increased from 1944—a low in sunspot activity—to a peak in 1948-49 when solar activity was intense. After the summer of 1949, paralleling the sunspot cycle, the voltage trend started downward. *Hence, graphs of annual tree field variations and relative sunspot numbers parallel each other.*

Though neither trees, plants nor seeds have nervous systems, it is interesting to note that the F_3F_4 maize seeds discussed in Chapter 4 showed higher voltage gradients in 1945 and 1946 than their precursors in 1943 and 1944. Burr could not account for this unexpected phenomenon.

It is also interesting to note that in 1801, in a communication to the Royal Society, Sir William Herschel concluded that from 1650-1713 a scarcity of vegetation, especially wheat, had occurred at every sunspot minimum, and suggested a relationship between sunspot cycles and seasonal yields of wheat or corn. A century later, his study was confirmed by Moreaux. Sir James Jeans, too, noted a progressive thickness of tree rings paralleling the sunspot cycle along with increasingly moist summers.

Independently, Markson has correlated tree potentials with geomagnetic variations. He concluded that either tree potentials respond directly to geomagnetic activity or that both may be under the influence of other geophysical factors.

These findings should not be interpreted as suggesting that the moon, the proximity of the earth to the sun or sunspots are themselves necessarily acting upon living systems. The evidence does suggest, however, that celestial forces interact with all charged particles, organic and inorganic. Therefore, Burr's pioneer experiments with trees and plants open up a vast area of useful research for future workers.

Organic matter is especially susceptible to celestial forces because it is composed of an incredibly complex flux of atomic particles in relative equilibrium within—and subject to—the electric field forces of the Universe. These all-pervasive forces not only govern the motions and velocities of the stars and planets through countless solar systems but also, somehow, affect the position and direction of the infinitesimal charged particles of which all living things are composed. As Northrop expressed it:

> Nature has put a bit of all of herself into even the most humble living creature.

Chapter Six

The Measurement of Hypnosis and Emotions

1

In the foregoing chapter, the reader will have noted some useful applications of the *Theory* in medicine, surgery, and agriculture. We have seen that by measuring the voltage gradients in the human electrodynamic field, it is possible to determine the time of ovulation, the rate of wound healing and to detect malignancy before there are any overt symptoms. We have seen, too, that such measurements allow us to predict the future vigor of seeds.

As more research is carried out, no doubt many other useful applications of the *Theory* will be discovered. In fact, it is perhaps no exaggeration to say that one day the measurement of electrodynamic fields will be an indispensable weapon in the armory of physicians, surgeons, psychiatrists and agriculturalists.

Meanwhile, the *Theory* has already opened up great opportunities for the better understanding and assessment of the emotional states of men and women.

It has already been noted that I obtained the first electrometric record of hypnosis and it may be of interest to tell how this came about.

Pasteur observed that "chance only favors the mind that is prepared" and my experience seems to endorse this. As a very young man, I had been trained in EEG interpretations and circuitry by A. J. Derbyshire, Ph.D., then of Harper Hospital, Detroit, Michigan. It was Derbyshire who with Hallowell Davis, M.D. introduced Hans Berger's EEG discovery into the United States at Massachusetts General Hospital and Harvard Medical School, Boston, Massachusetts in 1934.

Beginning in 1945, I was trained by Milton H. Erickson, M.D., the world's foremost authority on hypnosis, at Wayne County General Hospital, Eloise, Michigan, in the most sophisticated, empiric techniques of hypnosis which Erickson was developing. Erickson's elegant and imaginative experiments, using maverick procedures, were a great empiric advance in both hypnosis and psychiatry. Therefore, I had been sufficiently prepared for chance to grant a favor (as quoted earlier from Pasteur). This took the form of an invitation to a Yale party in the summer of 1947, given by the noted psychologists Walter R. and Catharine Cox Miles. A fellow guest at the party was Harold S. Burr, who later introduced me to Filmer S. C. Northrop.

After conversations with Burr about the Burr-Northrop *Theory*, it seemed logical to envisage the possibility of measuring hypnotic states. Burr agreed that this was possible, lent one of his instruments, and on the evening of April 24, 1948, the first field record of hypnosis known to me was obtained on neurologist Sue E. Browder, M.D.

By November 15, 1949, technical problems involving continuous field monitoring had been worked out under the personal supervision of Burr in the Section of Neuro-Anatomy, initially by using General Electric photoelectric recorders running at a speed of 2.54 cm/min and connected to the millivoltmeter. Field correlates of hypnosis first were presented in *Science*, 1950, followed by the first atlas of hypnotic tracings published by Tracy J. Putnam, M.D., then editor of *AMA Archives of Neurology and Psychiatry* and Director of Services, Neurological Institute Columbia-Presbyterian Medical Center, 1951. On August 28, 1959, a more sensitive cathode ray oscilloscope first was used to monitor hypnotic states in Burr's Yale Medical School office, Fig. 1.

These successful and exciting experiments naturally suggested other possibilities. If hypnotic states could produce measurable changes in the field, it seemed logical to assume that other states, such as emotions, could also be measured. In other words, here at last was a possible electronic means to measure emotional states, objectively, quantitatively and reproducibly.

FIG. 1. First hypnotic state measured on cathode ray oscilloscope connected to Burr-Lane-Nims millivoltmeter, B-250 SHM, Yale Medical School, August 28, 1959. Rémie Ross-Duggan Fenske with Dr. H. S. Burr in background.

2

Most people will agree that the human neocortex is one of the most important parts of man because it distinguishes him, not always favorably, from the less complex animals and all other forms of life on this planet.

Over the centuries, many theories have been advanced concerning the nature of its function in maintaining optimal human health. But whatever view is preferred, all will agree that too little is known for certain about a most important part of man and that it is of great practical urgency to add to our knowledge.

Nearly everyone knows of someone who is retarded or who is suffering from some brain defect. Many thousands, uneasy about their own emotional states, submit themselves, or are urged to submit themselves, to psychiatric treatment. And psychiatry, a relatively new science, is too often subjective and uncertain, and extremely expensive.

A high percentage of the hospital beds in every country is occupied by psychiatric patients—a heavy burden on the taxpayer. There are not enough reliable standards by which to judge whether a patient is fit enough to be released. In consequence, dangerous lunatics are sometimes turned loose on the community while patients who could safely be released are kept in needless and desolate custody.

For economic as well as humane reasons, then, it is imperative to find out more about human emotions, whatever they may be. Modern science has made its great advances largely because means have been devised to measure various phenomena. In fact, some scientists attempt to deny the reality of anything that cannot be measured. This, of course, is going too far. There are some directly sensed perceptions, such as beauty, which cannot be measured and yet none will deny that they exist.

Measurement, however, is an indispensable tool for the advancement of knowledge. As it is at last possible to measure emotional states objectively, quantitatively and reproducibly, we now have the means to learn more about them. Emotional states or conditions affect the voltage gradients in the human electrodynamic field and it is possible to measure these changing states simply and objectively with sensitive instruments.

In other words, the assessment of emotional states need no longer be purely subjective.

3

Apparently Burr had never considered the measurement of hypnotic phenomena until he saw it in his office in 1949. And it may be of interest to quote his comments on this experiment from his definitive work *Blueprint for Immortality*:

> His [Dr. Ravitz's] results are striking and extraordinary. Perhaps the most remarkable result obtained in our laboratory by Dr. Ravitz was when he found a significant electrometric correlate of hypnotism that was astonishing to watch: *a continuously-recording voltmeter showed evidence of marked changes in voltage gradient during the hypnotic process.*
>
> This was not an event which might be related to the subjectivity of the operator, but could be recorded without argument on the recording galvanometer. If anyone needed objective evidence of the results of hypnosis, one needed only to look at the charts recorded under these conditions...
>
> It becomes evident from Dr. Ravitz's examination that by using electro-metric techniques on patients in psychiatric hospitals, patients—as the result of therapy, or changing circumstances—could safely be discharged from the hospital when the voltage gradient indicated a reasonable return to normal. Likewise, electro-metrics could show clearly enough when certain patients—no matter what the therapy was—could *not* be returned safely to normal life outside of

the institution. The value of this to the institutionalized psychotic should be apparent at once.

Needless to say, a great deal more study is needed and much more data must be collected.

I also found electromagnetic field evidence supporting Erickson's clinical observations that subjects take at least twenty to thirty minutes to develop sufficiently deep hypnotic states for adequate experimental work including *true* memory revivifications. These electrometric findings also substantiated Erickson's clinical discovery that carrying out posthypnotic suggestions reestablishes the hypnotic state.

Furthermore, as previously noted by Erickson, no relationship exists between field measurements and classic empiric rating-scale criteria of hypnotic depth based on inductively inferred, directly observable factors. Some subjects who can experience complex phenomena are not in deep trances, and variability exists even within the same subjects at different times. This shows the limitations of subjective judgment and the advantage of objective, quantitative, reproducible electrometric measurement.

Moreover, here at last was a means of obtaining objective evidence which confirmed Erickson's clinical observations that hypnotic states can and do arise spontaneously during intense concentration. For instance, in concentrating on his writing, an author can be in a state of self-hypnosis, oblivious to surroundings or interruptions which are not inimical to his welfare, even though there is no hypnotist present.

Erickson also emphasized that neuromuscular and other changes accompany hypnotic states in many subjects, a fact to which few psychologists and psychiatrists have paid any attention. These include ocular fixation; pupillary changes; sclerae alterations; altered eyeblink reflexes; muscular rigidity with set facial expression; sitting, standing and turning in one piece—some alterations resembling paralysis agitans without the tremors, as I pointed out in 1958. These may reappear with typical EMF correlates during responses to posthypnotic suggestions. Occasionally, athetoid and choreiform movements have developed spontaneously and in one instance at Yale Medical School, 1960, camptocormia, Figs. 2 and 3. The more common neuromuscular changes occur spontaneously in numerous individuals, persons who disclaim ever having been "hypnotized." Field measurements of such persons after such physiologic alterations have been observed are indistinguishable from trance states induced by another person. Almost invariably such individuals, when questioned, indicate thinking about something at the time. This suggests that at the very least, many individuals go into spontaneous trance states without recognizing them as such.

FIG. 2. Spontaneous athetoid movements during hypnotic state, Philadelphia, PA, 1960. Dr. Juan Carlos De Tata.

FIG. 3. Spontaneous camptocormia, B-250 SHM, Yale Medical School, 1960. Dr. Juan Carlos De Tata. Dr. Lewis R. Roddy and Dr. H. S. Burr in background.

Such findings are of critical importance in experimental work which claims to study groups of "scientifically observed" subjects supposedly hypnotized, versus those who, because they have not been subjected to some ritualistic induction procedure, are thought to be in nonhypnotic waking states. The further spuriousness of such pseudo-scientific experiments is evidenced when the experimenters are not conversant with all of the observable nuances of trance states including the frequently noted neuromuscular changes. Recognition of such state changes is especially important to those interested in obtaining nonhypnotic waking field records as the voltage shifts accompanying hypnosis may be most profound. This suggests a need to reformulate definitions of hypnosis in terms of field intensity, **E** and polarity, **H** variables, which would include meditation-related empiric operational procedures as well as spontaneous trance states which are independent of other persons.

4

EMF tracings show the following characteristic field shifts during both hypnosis and posthypnotic suggestions and are affected by the subject's behavior, health and emotional state:

(1) After a variable induction phase, sometimes characterized by relatively rapid (12 to 15/min) EMF oscillations, particularly during catalepsy, the tracing smoothes, losing its usual variable nonhypnotic waking pattern as gradual field detensifications or less frequent intensifications occur. This may vary in the same subject at different times and may be minimal in experienced hypnotic subjects at given times, depending on their prehypnotic EMF baseline intensity. In this way the concept of hypnotic depth has been redefined in terms of relative EMF changes from the prehypnotic baseline state.

(2) At the instrument sensitivity used, speaking and eyes open do not affect EMF tracings except in light hypnotic states, the record then reverting to nonhypnotic waking state configurations.

(3) Dreams, hallucinations and regressions alter the typical tracing minimally, if at all, unless associated with emotions.

(4) Emotions, such as anxiety and grief, cause EMF intensifications of either plus or minus polarity, providing quantitative measures of affective responses at given times in whatever hypnotic or nonhypnotic configurations they appear.

(5) Startle responses, itching, scratching, throat tickling, coughing sensation, coughing, sneezing sensation, sneezing, hiccoughing sensation, hiccoughing, pain, headache, nausea, vomiting and gastrointestinal cramps produce a similar picture to that found under drugs, in sleep or during gaseous inhalations.

(6) Euphoria, loquaciousness, general excitability and ovulation (Fig. 4) before, during or after hypnosis produce a consistently irregular high-intensity pattern like that found under drugs and during gaseous inhalations. Variations in hypnotic tracings are thus affected by changes in the subject's energy level rather than by any specific procedure or isolated experimental phenomenon.

(7) EMF shifts in the plus polarity direction usually occur at trance termination, often exceeding +*30* mv in those experiencing deep hypnotic states defined electrometrically. The length of time before the record reverts to the nonhypnotic waking state measures the rapidity of the subject's arousal. Some subjects show rapid arousal, some slow, others slip in and out of trance states until finally shifting into nonhypnotic waking states and many vary from time to time. Subjects who have been aroused but who actually are only partially aroused or return to the trance state, though superficially appearing to be in nonhypnotic waking states, show field correlates of such state changes.

(8) Field monitoring can detect simulators instantly as well as spontaneous autohypnotic states in those thought by the experimenter to be in nonhypnotic waking states.

(9) Field records of subjects acting on posthypnotic suggestions substantiate Erickson's original clinical observations that a reversion to the hypnotic state occurs at these times.

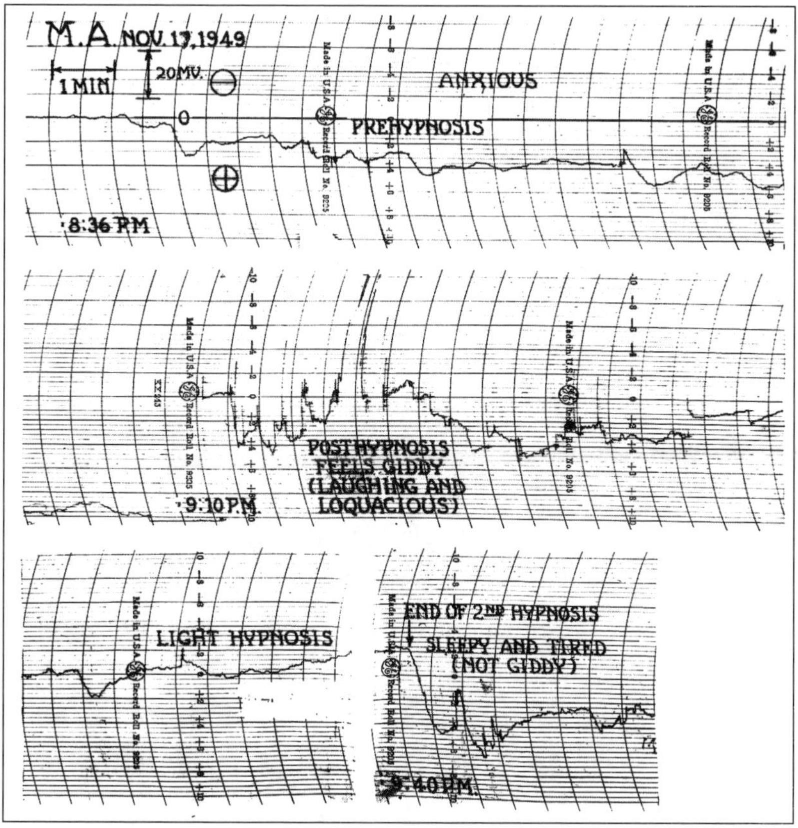

FIG. 4. (read from left to right) EMF tracing showing presumed ovulation following first hypnotic state, B-248 SHM, Yale Medical School, November 17, 1949. (Published in L. J. Ravitz: Standing potential correlates of hypnosis and narcosis. *AMA Arch. Neurol. Psychiat.* 65:413-436, 1951; and in H. S. Burr: *Blueprint for Immortality: The Electric Patterns of Life*. London & Sudbury, Suffolk, England: Neville Spearman 1972, 1977, 1982, 1988.)

5

Comparison of hypnotic EMF records with those of other states, such as sleep, insulin coma, use of barbiturates or amphetamines and electroshock, shows certain similarities and differences. For example:

(1) EMF tracings during sleep cannot be distinguished from hypnotic tracings when they decrease in intensity. However, whereas sleep produces marked EEG changes, EEG changes during hypnosis present a waking state pattern with only minor variations due to shifts in alertness unless hypnosis blends into sleep automatically or as a result of suggestions.* Drowsy states cause field detensifications as well as characteristic EEG changes. This is to be expected if we consider that improved discrimination and concentration can occur during hypnosis, whereas EEG alterations appear in sleep. Table 1 summarizes certain common factors producing EMF and/or EEG changes. Those which show EMF variations demonstrate the basic nature of field phenomena in living matter.

(2) Autohypnotic and hypnotic states produce the same EMF patterns as do posthypnotic suggestions, meditation-related procedures and hypnotic states effected via the "water binge," an ideosensory-ideomotor technique invented by me, effected by drinking varying quantities of water.

(3) Hypoxia or hypercapnea, whether from CO_2-O_2 mixture, N_2O-O_2 or other gaseous inhalations, produces marked changes both in the EMF and EEG patterns, the requisite amount needed to produce desired experimental or therapeutic state shifts correlating with field strengths of the variable EMF baseline state prior to administration. Moreover, the evocation of state perturbations through such procedures provides another index of "personality"

*As originally discovered by Burr and Barton, EMF records can monitor depth of sleep even with electrodes on symphysis and vagina. The first simultaneous EMF-EEG recordings were taken by King.

stability at any given time.

(4) Insulin coma or coma resulting from other factors also changes both EMF and EEG patterns. Likewise, correlates have been found between EMF intensifications and lack of insulin reaction to usual coma dosage. On the other hand, postcoma insulin reactions (i.e., returning to a comatose state) were noted in patients who were rapidly decelerating on their diurnal EMF curves.

(5) Placebos, with or without appropriate verbal suggestions, have at times produced concomitant neuromuscular and EMF changes indistinguishable from those seen in hypnosis and which are often associated with profound changes in statefunction. This occurs in the absence of significant EEG alterations.

(6) Electroshock appears to dampen EMF intensifications after

TABLE 1
SUMMARY OF CERTAIN COMMON FACTORS PRODUCING EMF AND/OR EEG CHANGES

Maximal EMF	EMF axes on unfertilized frog eggs define longitudinal embryo axes after fertilization; rotating salamanders, coppersolder robots generate parallel EMF's in enveloping *saline* v. no glass-rod EMF; from imposed EMF's on exercised frog sciatic nerves, record propagated impulses in surrounding *air* — measured values falling on math-predicted curves; predict seed growth capacities, morphogenesis, future size, vitality, hybid vigor; alter slime-mold growth orientation by fixed imposed EMF's; non-brain malignancies; peripheral nerve injuries, wounds, healing; ataraxics; hydrotherapy; ovulation; arthritis, allergies, peptic ulcers, recovery; parallel electrocyclic phenomena: periodic movements of several frequencies in atmosphere, earth, life forms; recorded values fall on math-predicted curves, correlate with geomagnetic variations, provide certain short- and long-range predictions; hypnotic-autohypnotic states, carrying out posthypnotic sugestions.
Maximal EMF — variable EEG	Pain, migraine, nausea, vomiting, gastrointestinal cramps; systemic illness, recovery; sneezing sensation, sneezing, itching, scratching, aching, throat tickling, coughing sensation, coughing, hiccoughing, yawning; dreams, other hallucinations involving emotions; sudden emotion esp. fright, rage, embarrassment, startle responses; depressed, euphoric, hypomanic-manic states, loquaciousness, excitability, acute psychotic episodes, behavior disorders involving emotion: excitation → exhaustion.
Maximal EMF — maximal EEG	Drowsiness, sleep depth; hypoxia, hypercapnea, gaseous anesthetics; insulin coma or coma resulting from other factors; seizure states; delirium; brain maligancies; infancy, youth, aging, death.
Variable EMF	Placebos, if spontaneous hypnotic states thereby produced.
Maximal EEG — variable EMF	Postelectroshock states.
Maximal EEG	Cortical stimulants and depressants, e.g., barbiturates, bromides, alcohol, caffeine, amphetamines; dilantin; thyroxin.
Variable EEG	Vasodilators, vasoconstrictors.

blished in L. J. Ravitz: EEG correlates of hypnotically-revivified seizures. *J. Am. Soc. Psychosom. Dent. Med.* 29: 128-140, 1982.)

varying lengths of time, with initial cortical disruption as reflected in convulsive EEG patterns.

(7) Sodium amytal narcosis evokes minimal EMF and maximal EEG changes, as do other *barbiturates, bromides, and amphetamines,* unless associated with an augmentation or quelling of state disquietudes such as general excitability. Voltage shifts of considerable magnitude which sometime accompany hypnotic induction are rarely present, and the gradual wearing off of the drug effect precludes any considerable terminal voltage shifts. Tranquilizers, on the other hand, can profoundly affect the field.

(8) Resistance to hypnosis may be lowered or mobilized under narcosis. Due to a physiologic depression of the cortex, hypnotic states are less satisfactory in conjunction with sodium amytal, or for that matter, with the use of any drug.

6

Hypnotic depth can now be quantitatively assessed through field measurements. The deepest electrometric states, as previously noted, are not necessarily associated with traditional criteria for determining hypnotic depth—such as amnesia, negative hallucinations, etc. —but only with the magnitude of relative voltage change (whether decreased or increased) from that of the nonhypnotic waking pattern and the amount of smoothing. Any disturbance of the hypnotic state can be detected immediately by voltage intensifications and loss of the straight-line configuration.

7

The first public demonstrations of field monitoring were conducted at the Second Annual Scientific Assembly of the American

Society of Clinical Hypnosis, 1452 LaSalle Hotel, Chicago, Illinois. On Saturday, October 10, 1959, at 11:17 a.m., Dee Dee Steinfuhr demonstrated autohypnosis even before the electrodes were fastened and the instruments activated. Observationally, she showed mask-like face, pupillary dilation, ocular fixation, and loss of eye-blink reflexes, Fig. 5a, the tracing recording a typical hypnotic straight-line configuration hovering about the zero baseline, Fig. 5b. Slight arousal at about 11:19 a.m. correlated with a brief + 6 mv EMF intensification.

FIG. 5a. Autohypnotic state demonstrated by Dee Dee Steinfuhr, October 10, 1959, Chicago, IL.

An example of the effect of certain body sensations on field intensities during hypnosis occurred at the Chicago demonstrations. Elizabeth M. Erickson, who likewise is well experienced with trance states, also demonstrated autohypnosis—again the straight-line configuration indicating that she was in a light trance state when the instruments were activated at 12:03 p.m., Figs. 6a and 6b. The field intensity ranged from +*4* to +*5* mv, rising briefly to +*10* mv, and again stabilizing between +*8* and +2 mv. During her induction phase which represented a deepening procedure, around 12:06 p.m., the pattern suddenly shifted to +*12* mv with some low voltage fast frequencies, detensifying to +2 mv and stabilizing in thirty seconds at +*9* to +*10* mv. At 12:11 p.m. the pattern suddenly shifted from +*3* to +*13* mv, again with some low voltage fast frequencies, and by 12:12 p.m. stabilized again at +*9* to +*10* mv. Later she reported that during this interval her throat was tickling and she felt like coughing, a sensation which recurred at 12:20 p.m. to a lesser degree, lasting only thirty seconds, with a smooth intensification from +*4* to +*9* mv. During arousal, which began about 12:29 p.m., low voltage fast frequencies appeared with one spike to -*2* mv—probably an artifact—the record stabilizing at about her originally recorded intensity in the +10 mv range.

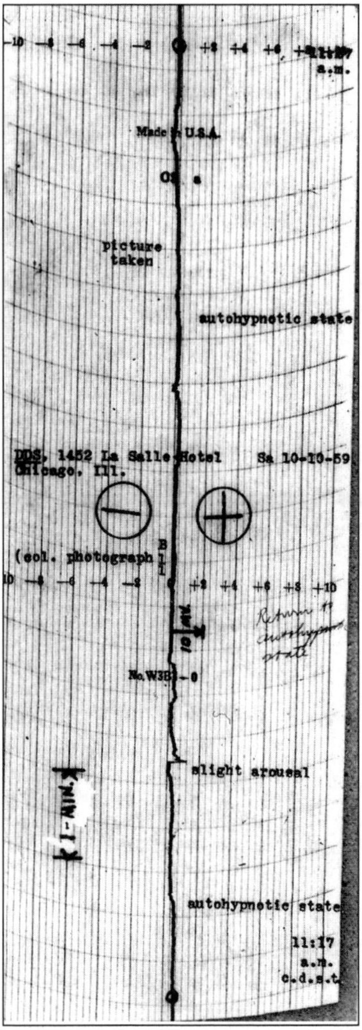

FIG. 5b. (read from bottom to top) EMF tracing of autohypnotic state, Fig. 5a.

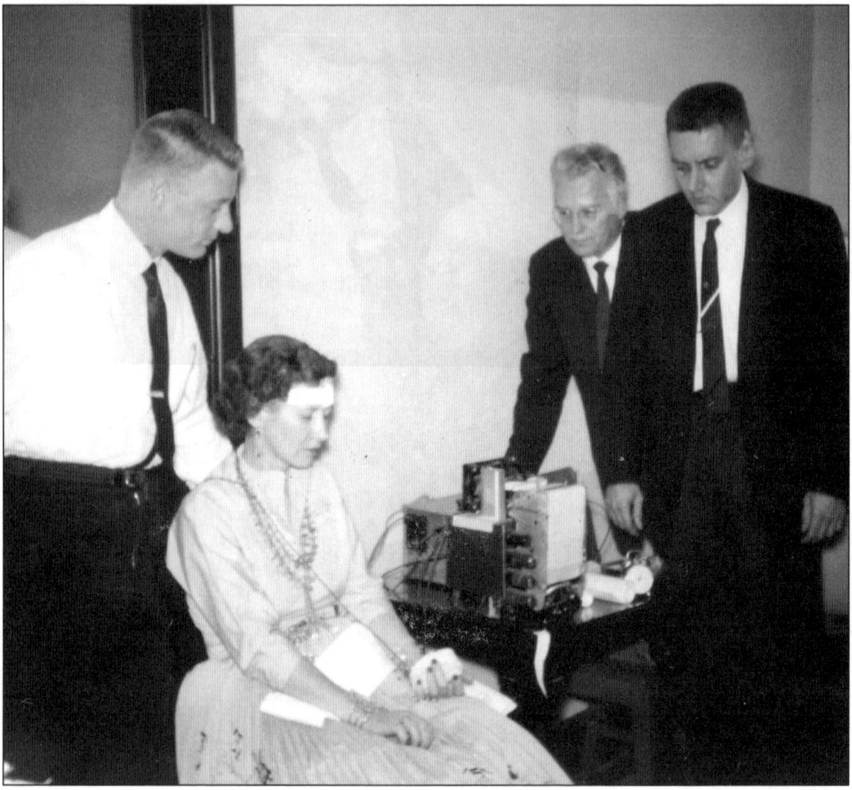

FIG. 6a. Autohypnotic state demonstrated by Elizabeth M. Erickson, October 10, 1959, Chicago, IL. Left to right Warren J. Elliott, Elizabeth M. Erickson, Dr. Wm. F. Blair, & Dr. L. J. Ravitz. (Published in H. S. Burr: *Blueprint for Immorality*: Neville Spearman 1972, 1977, 1982, 1988.)

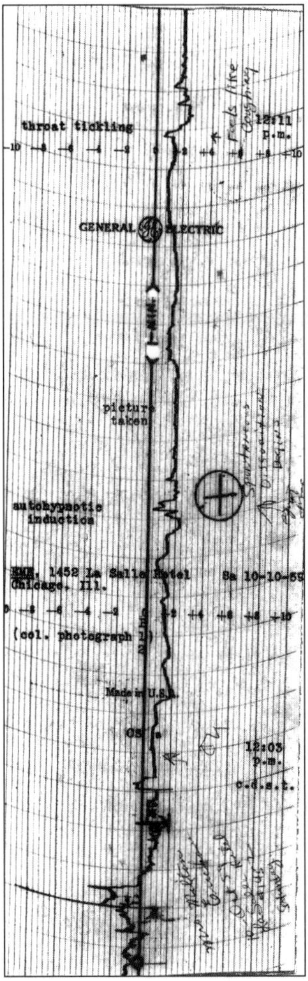

FIG. 6b. (read from left to right) EMF tracing of autohypnotic state, Fig. 6a, showing voltage increases during sensations of throat tickling.

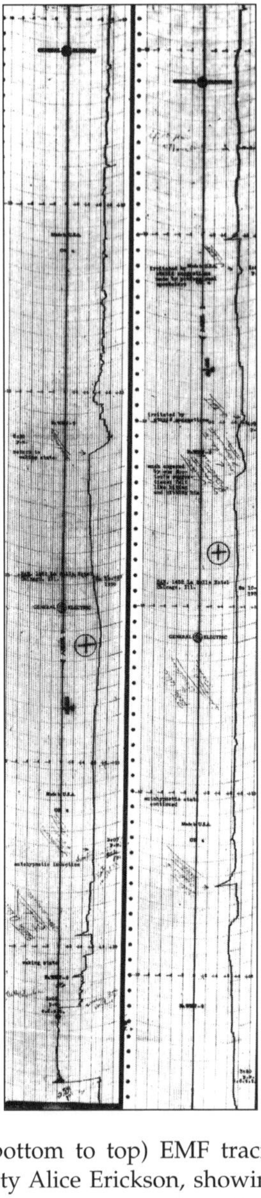

FIG. 7. (read from bottom to top) EMF tracing of autohypnotic state demonstrated by Betty Alice Erickson, showing voltage intensifications during irritation and anger, October 10, 1959, Chicago, IL.

The same afternoon, field correlates of anger were obtained. Beginning at 3:07 p.m., Betty Alice Erickson also demonstrated autohypnosis for over two hours, Fig. 7. At about 3:20 p.m. on arousal, her +*22* mv straight-line tracing intensified to +*42* mv, stabilizing in a nonhypnotic waking pattern ranging from +*24* to +*32* mv after a two-minute transition period, but soon developing the straight-line configuration characteristic of hypnotic states. Through numerous suggestions from the audience, her autohypnotic state continued relatively uninterrupted until 3:59 p.m. A ninety-second field intensification, from +*30* to +*39* mv, associated with low-voltage faster frequencies, stabilized at +*31* mv at about 4:01 p.m. As reported, much angered by one doctor's suggestions, interpreted as *ordering* her to go into a deeper trance state, she "felt like biting and hitting him" for an estimated thirty seconds. Immediately afterwards, during a fifteen-second intensification to +*38* mv, Betty Alice merely felt irritated by "stupid suggestions" made by another onlooker. Her final fifteen-second burst of irritability was recorded at 4:06 p.m., the EMF intensifying from +*31* mv to a brief +*35* mv maximum, then stabilizing at +*32* mv. Betty Alice's younger age relative to that of her mother, Elizabeth M. Erickson, may account, in part, for the former's higher baseline EMF intensity.

8

Demonstrations at the Chicago convention were also conducted by Warren J. Elliott, who met with Professor Harold S. Burr for preliminary testing. The delicate equipment had been driven from New Haven to Chicago in a Citroën. Elliott, feeling anxious, had been experiencing mild nonspecific gastrointestinal symptoms. During a trial run, personally supervised by Burr in Burr's laboratory, B250 SHM, Yale Medical School, on Tuesday, October 6, 1959, Elliott's field tracing showed a relatively rare head-palm intensification of minus polarity (hi-minus). As the head is usually positive to the palm, such head-palm measurements are typically of plus polarity.

This unusual hi-minus head-palm reading correlated with the mild nonspecific gastrointestinal symptoms which the anxious subject was experiencing. At cataleptic trance induction, 10:22 a.m., the *-38* mv voltage gradient smoothed, reading *-44* mv prior to the hand touching the forehead at about 10:24 a.m. His baseline then shifted to *-47* mv. A thirty-second voltage shift from *-46* to *-37* mv accompanied the hand reaching the lap at 10:27 a.m. Trance termination at 10:36 a.m. correlated with a typical forty-five-second voltage excursion from *-43* to *-22* mv—the tracing gradually shifting in the minus direction with another plus shift in thirty seconds, from *-35* to *-26* mv, then gradually moving again in the minus direction with some minor voltage variations as he spontaneously returned to the hypnotic state. At 10:38 a.m., he suddenly became "more alert," the tracing intensifying in the plus direction, from *-42* to *-24* mv, then immediately shifting in the minus direction as he returned to a hypnotic state showing a variable straight-line pattern which registered *-44* mv at about 10:40 a.m. when the experiment terminated.

During a pleasant, uneventful drive without problems, from New Haven to New York to Chicago, the subject's anxiety state and gastrointestinal symptoms dissolved, and a second pre-demonstration test run was begun on Thursday, October 8, 1959, in suite 1452 LaSalle Hotel, Chicago, 3:53 p.m. His previously induced trance state deepened and the EMF intensified from *0* to *+8* to *+10* mv thirty seconds later. By fits and starts, the straight-line intensification continued until 4:44 p.m., when at *+28* mv a suggestion for arousal was given. A *+2* mv intensification lasting about ten seconds followed, detensifying suddenly from *+30* to *+28* mv and continuing in a straight-line pattern for about seventy-five seconds. Then at 4:46 p.m., the *+25* mv field pattern intensified to *+27* mv, suddenly detensified to a *+17* mv field pattern, again intensified to *+27* mv and suddenly detensified to *+17* mv. Elliott sat forward in his chair, and with eyes open and conversing in a light hypnotic state, terminated the experiment at about 4:47 p.m.

Additional demonstrations with Elliott provided some unexpected information which showed that both achieving a satisfactory trance state and its successful field measurements are affected by external events as well as internal factors.

To accommodate the anticipated audience for the first public demonstrations on Friday, October 9, 1959, the monitoring equipment was moved up to the 19th-floor Century Room near the elevators and, beginning at 9:50 a.m., another trial run was attempted by the demonstrator on himself. The penwriter jiggled off the recording paper; the electrodes failed to reverse; and as the millivoltmeter, photoelectric recorder and electrodes showed no obvious defects, interfering fields caused by the elevators were suspected. Having expended enormous time and effort to conduct an important demonstration, Elliott, the operator, was noticeably upset. However, by 11:50 a.m., with less elevator activity, valid measurements with electrode reversibility were obtained for short intervals. Elliott's EMF showed a dramatic accentuation of plus polarity ranging from *+62* to *+44* mv, Fig. 8. Cataleptic trance induction at 11:51 a.m. was accompanied by a sudden intensification to *+60* mv, followed by detensification in fifteen seconds to *+50* mv then by a hi-plus pattern of great variability. Even the arrival of the cataleptic arm to his lap at 11:57 a.m. was not associated with EMF changes beyond the marked variability which preceded this. Such hi-plus variability continued, peaking at *+72* mv at 12:03 p.m., showing occasional brief straight-line runs. Following one of these rare thirty-second straight-line configurations at *+60* mv, the subject was aroused at 12:06 p.m. In ten seconds, a rapid 34 mv detensification to *+26* mv occurred, though variable *+18* to *+52* mv high voltage spikes appeared, and Elliott remained very upset. After the monitoring ended at 12:10 p.m., the equipment was moved down to suite 1452 for the demonstrations, far from the elevators.

It is difficult to effect hetero- or autohypnotic states when relative field strengths are high (either plus or minus polarity). This is why it is hard to produce hypnotic states in acutely disturbed persons.

Field measurement interference was also experienced during the October 1978 demonstrations with Kenneth A. Bartlett Jr., D.D.S. at the 21st annual meeting of the American Society of Clinical Hypnosis, Chase-Park Plaza Hotel, St. Louis, Missouri, this time caused by a huge TV microwave transmitter/receiver about thirty feet east of the Chase building. However, the last demonstrations proceeded satisfactorily in the Park Plaza building which was shielded by the Chase complex.

Over the next forty-eight-hour period, Elliott's field picture showed a rubber-band rebound effect with a voltage shift from hi-plus EMF of marked variability with emotional upset (caused by the interference of the elevators and the inability to obtain many valid measurements) to a hi-minus pattern, rare with head-palm electrode placements, again correlating with gastrointestinal upset and diarrhea.

During late afternoon Saturday, Elliott had developed gastrointestinal symptoms with diarrhea and felt ill by the time of the last demonstrations on Sunday, October 11, 1959. Again he used himself as a subject, hoping that a hypnotic state would mitigate his symptoms.

A spontaneous autohypnotic state occurred with muscle rigidity, ocular fixation and loss of eyeblink reflex as soon as the subject applied the electrodes to himself at 10:56 a.m. At 11:00 a.m., when the instruments were in operation, he closed his eyes. The EMF tracing registered a straight-line pattern of *-36* mv, which slowly intensified to *-38* mv. By the time of the demonstration photograph

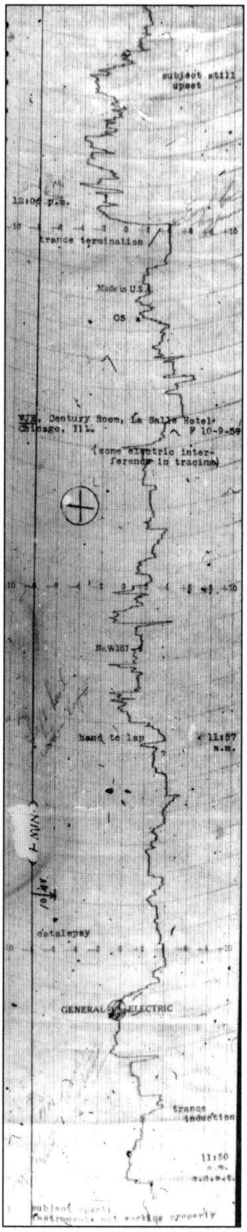

FIG. 8. (read from bottom to top) EMF tracing of Warren J. Elliott showing marked variable voltage intensifications during disturbed state, October 9, 1959, Chicago, IL.

at 11:12 a.m., the EMF had detensified to *-32* mv, Figs. 9a and 9b. As before, only the record segment visible on the photoelectric recorder at the time the subject was photographed is reproduced. After taking the picture, I left the room with Marion Moore, M.D. in charge, who made repeated suggestions for hypnotic deepening at 11:14 and 11:19 a.m.—many observers believing that Moore had hypnotized the subject. Gradual EMF detensification continued. At 11:25 a.m., I walked into the room and spoke to Dr. Moore, who noted such events on the recording paper, making no comments to Elliott, whose EMF suddenly detensified from *-26* to *-24* mv, Fig. 9c. At 11:36 a.m., Moore made further suggestions, accompanied by EMF intensification to *-34* mv, Figs. 9d and 9e.

FIG. 9a. Autohypnotic state demonstrated by Warren J. Elliott, October 11, 1959, Chicago, IL.

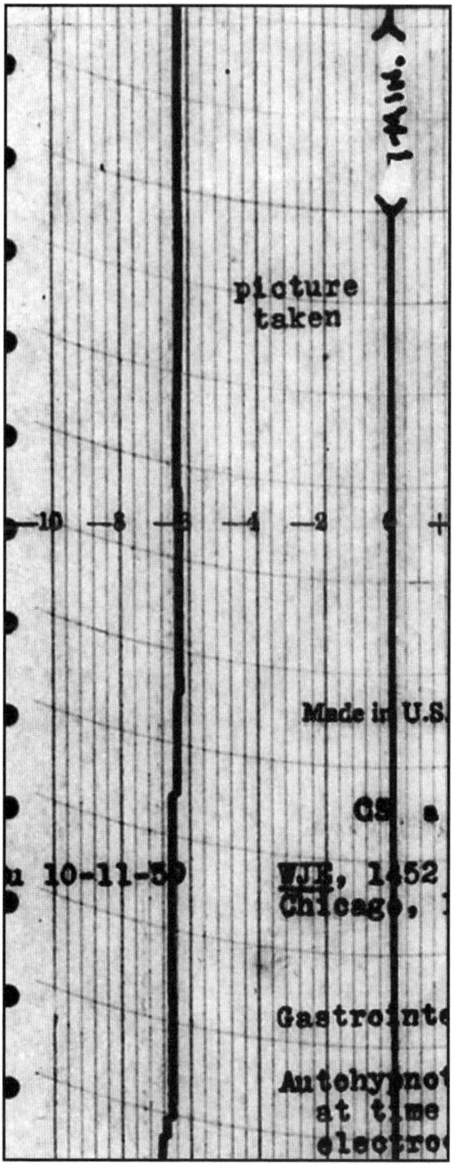

FIG. 9b. (read from left to right) EMF tracing of autohypnotic state, showing hi-minus pattern correlating with gastrointestinal symptoms, Fig. 9a.

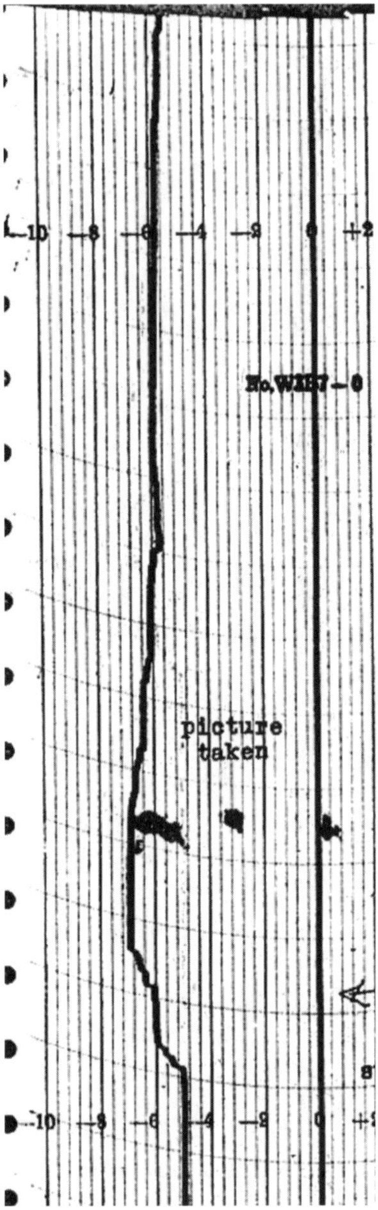

FIG. 9c. (read from left to right) Slight EMF detensification during repeated suggestions for hypnotic deepening.

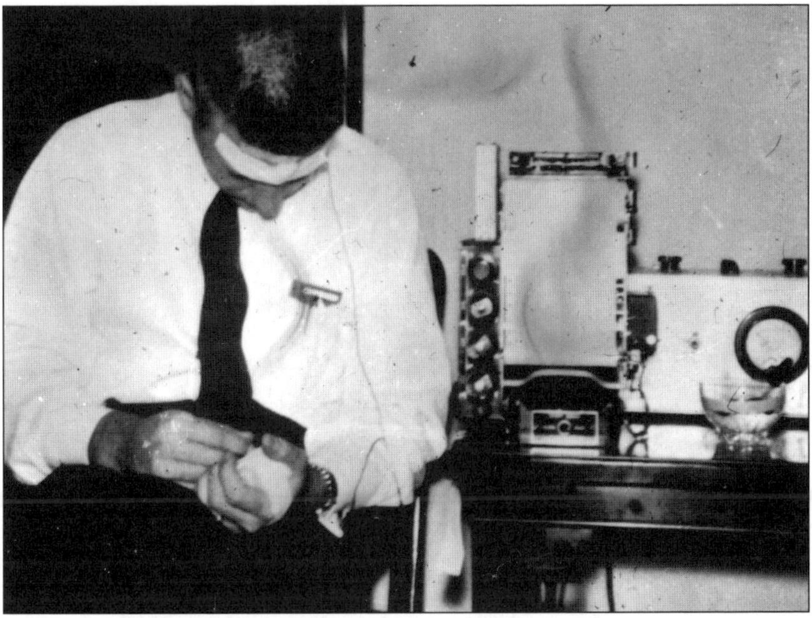

FIG. 9d. Autohypnotic state after further suggestions.

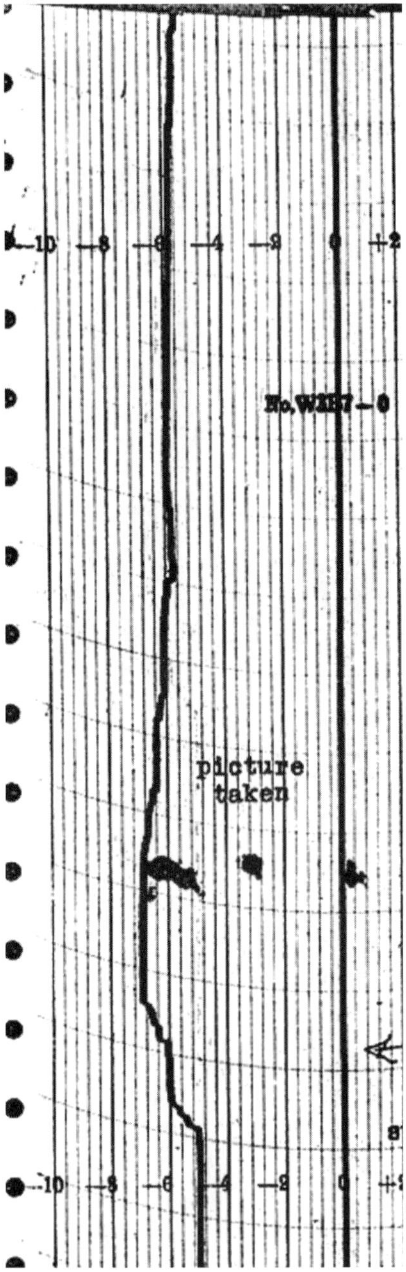

FIG. 9e. (read from left to right) EMF intensification after further suggestions, Fig. 9d.

Elliott's final demonstration of hypnosis disproved some conventional and stereotyped ideas about the trance state. After his arousal, Elliott spontaneously returned to a hypnotic state though his eyes were open and his appearance didn't fit the usual description of a hypnotized subject. Further, there had been no formal induction. However, EMF measurements were able to show the autohypnotic trance state as well as a general feeling of improved well-being following his EMF detensification.

At an attempted arousal shortly after 11:43 a.m., Elliott's EMF reading was *-28* mv. Slight initial detensification to *-26* mv was followed in the next twenty seconds by fast low-voltage intensifications between *-31* and *-29* mv and then by a straight-line intensification to *-38* mv indicating that he had spontaneously returned to an auto-hypnotic state. The subject was seated with eyes open and considered fully aroused by many members of the audience, and at about ninety seconds after initial arousal, he was asked to stand. This resulted in a rapid *+11* mv detensification to *-27* mv, which with one minor blip increased to a *-32* mv straight-line plateau. About six minutes after a suggestion to stand, a photograph was taken at 11:51 a.m. for documentation when the subject again was seated, Figs. 9f and 9g.

Clinical correlates of Elliott's autohypnotic state, though supposedly aroused, were fixed facial expression, ocular fixation, pupillary dilation and absent eyeblink reflex. Another hypnotic termination was attempted at 11:54 a.m., resulting first in a rapid EMF intensification to *-40* mv, immediately followed by detensification and a polar reversal to *+17* mv with a variable detensifying EMF pattern gradually approaching the straight-line configuration as he went into another much lighter autohypnotic state. At this point, the instruments were turned off. However, as he said that he felt much better, more energetic and alert, despite a fixed smile with pupillary dilation, he was considered fully aroused by the audience. Later he confessed that he returned to an autohypnotic state to tune out a heated altercation between the observer sitting on his right, Fig. 9f, and myself.

Reactions of the observers to these demonstrations were mixed. Some maintained that autohypnotic states could not represent hypnosis without formal induction techniques, even though specific induction procedures produced the same EMF and clinical results. Others emotionally denied the validity of these objective, quantitative and reproducible measures of hypnotic states because they bore no relationship to the generally accepted empirically derived rating scales of hypnotic depth.

An original Burr-Lane-Nims millivoltmeter attached to a General Electric photoelectric recorder is shown in Figs. 5a, 6a, 9a, 9d, and 9f. For these experiments, specially designed electrodes were employed. Again, these were nonpolarizing silver-silver chloride electrodes (now commercially available). Moistened pads of isotonic saline solution were inserted between the electrodes and the skin to prevent metal-induced artifacts in this sort of measurement. (Commercial saline electrode paste is now used.) Placement of electrodes was standardized, one being strapped to the forehead and the other to the palm of either hand.

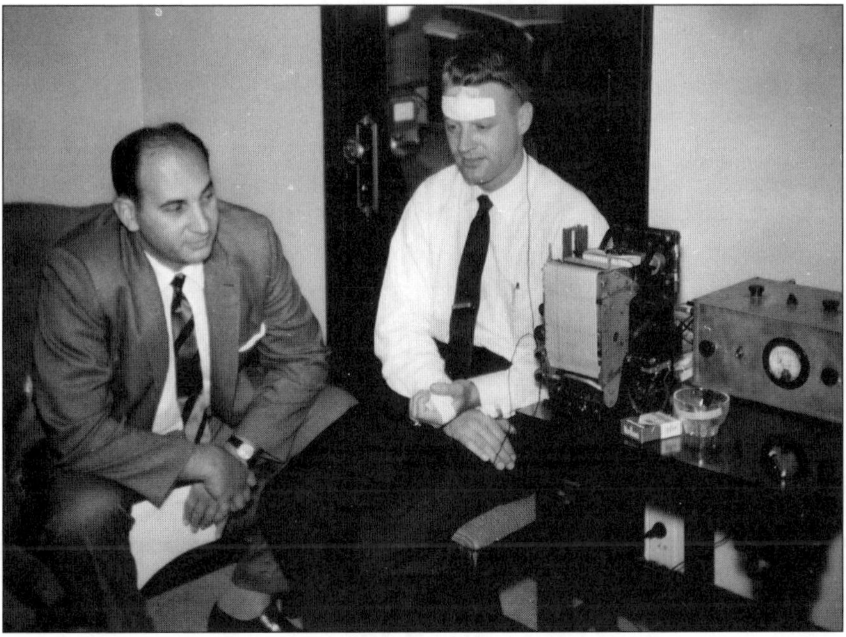

FIG. 9f. Spontaneous return to hypnotic state following arousal. Dr. Seymour Hershman to the left.

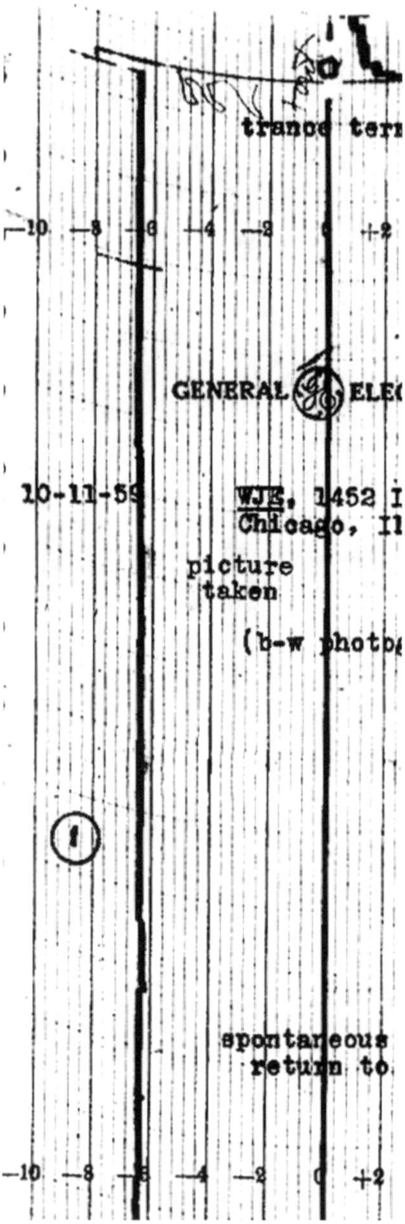

FIG. 9g. (read from left to right) EMF intensification at trance termination followed by spontaneous return to hypnotic state with eyes open, Fig. 9f.

In addition to such continuous monitoring with a strip-chart recorder, spot determinations were also made between forehead and anterior chest wall. An average was obtained from two series of readings taken from the right and left sides of the forehead and right and left anterior chest wall: (1) right head-right chest, (2) right head-left chest, (3) left head-right chest, and (4) left head-left chest. Results were then averaged with a second series of four measurements.

Incidentally, a similar procedure was followed in measuring parakeets in 1954. As the electrodes were large and the bodies small, parakeet measurements represent an average of the same eight head-chest leads.

With spot determinations, the average reading is expressed by two figures. The first indicates intensity without regard to polarity. This is the **E** quantity. The second figure denotes the dominant polarity or **H** quantity. For example, 30 *+30* mv indicates 30 mv intensity of uniform plus polarity. On the other hand, 30 *+10* mv shows the same 30 mv intensity of mixed plus and minus polarity, with a slightly dominant plus direction or spin.

In reviewing spot determination records of mixed polarity readings—usually indicating changing field transition states—specific leads and body sides showing plus and minus polarity can readily be ascertained.

One of the original millivoltmeters used at Duke Hospital, Durham, North Carolina, in late autumn 1951 is shown in Fig. 10. Fig. 4 shows presumed ovulation in a subject following her initial hypnosis in the Section of Neuro-Anatomy, Yale University Medical School on November 17, 1949 at 9:10 p.m. Forehead and palm electrode placements were used. To eliminate the possibility of purely emotional factors, measurements of field intensifications characteristic of ovulation were also obtained between right and left fingers. This was done by successively dipping the corresponding fingers of each hand into beakers of saline each containing an electrode attached to the millivoltmeter. Hangnails and cuts, if present, will produce injury potentials with this method.

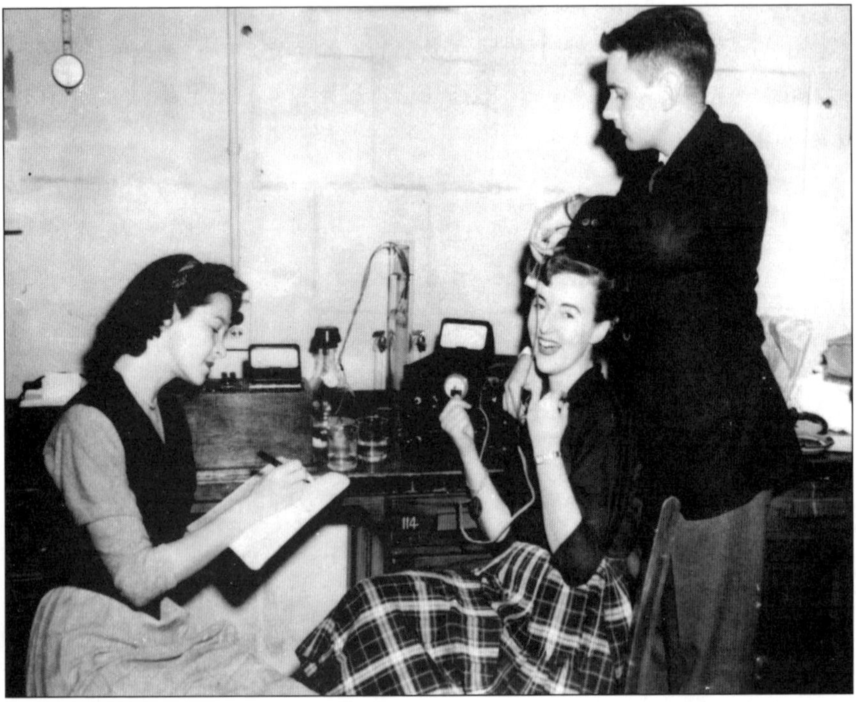

FIG. 10. Taking spot determinations of voltage gradients with an original Burr-Lane-Nims millivoltmeter, Duke Medical School, Durham, NC, autumn 1951. Alice Johnston, Rémie Ross-Duggan Fenske, and Dr. Leonard Ravitz.

Because the needle went off the scale, the exact magnitude of the subject's voltage rise could not be determined, though it exceeded 100 mv. The subject felt giddy and was laughing and loquacious. At the end of the second hypnosis at 9:40 p.m. voltages were much lower and the subject only felt sleepy and tired.

As we have seen, the voltage gradients of the electrodynamic field reflect the whole gamut of human conditions, both emotional and physical. And this is not confined simply to present conditions. Hypnotic recall of past events can also induce changes in the voltage gradients.

In his classic experiments on the human brain, Wilder Penfield was able to induce elderly patients, under local anesthetic, to recall and recount memories of childhood by electrostimulating certain areas of the cortex. This shows that memories of early childhood are somehow retained indefinitely, despite the constant metabolism of the brain cells.

For some unknown reason, Penfield seems to have revived only pleasant or harmless memories. Hypnosis, on the other hand, also can revive unpleasant or even terrifying memories.

In most healthy people, nature seems to draw a merciful curtain across unpleasant memories of the past and they tend to remember only happy and pleasant experiences. Some people, on the other hand, seem to lack this curtain and cherish memories of past grievances or injuries to the detriment of their emotional health, as every psychiatrist knows.

Few have not experienced some unpleasant or terrifying experience in the course of their lives. Even if these are not consciously remembered, they are permanently stored in the brain and may, like some internal festering ulcer, have adverse effects on emotional health. Curtain or not, hypnosis can usually expose these memories to the light of examination and thus help to remove any deleterious effects.

Now that it is possible to measure both hypnosis and the intensity of emotions (whether present or revivified past), the therapist is able to assess their relative potential for affecting the health of the patient. This will be discussed further in future chapters.

Chapter Seven

Electromagnetic Field–Neurocybernetic Theory of Hypnotic States

Field monitoring of changing statefunction, including hypnotic states together with their many manifestations, confirmed by Bartlett, Blagg, Rossi and Kost independently, has resulted in deductive considerations entailing the meshing of two radically disparate approaches: the Burr-Northrop field construct with its derivative instrumentation catalyzed by Maxwell and Gibbs, and a unified tripartite logic formalized mathematically by Fonseca in 1970.*

1

The field theory of hypnosis—proposed at the first annual meeting of the American Society of Clinical Hypnosis, Chicago, on October 3, 1958 as one of the basic factors in hypnotic states—derives from experimental knowledge of various factors and states which do and do not produce EMF variations. Table 1 includes various phylogenetically primitive subcortical factors inducing emotions and other energy perturbations which produce EMF changes, those effecting EEG alterations, and those states and other factors causing both EMF and EEG changes. Such observations are reinforced by the frequent spontaneous clinical manifestations of trance states, again involving this ancient brain core, further implicated by its potential control of physiologic survival functions via hypno-

* This was based on the studies of McCulloch, Pitts, Kilmer, Rosenblueth, Wiener and Bigelow, among others, including the epistemologic analyses and suggestions of Northrop.

sis—including the control of bleeding.

Briefly, all evidence suggests that profound alterations occur in the balance of the ancient centers with respect to the neocortex during hypnosis, with intact, or frequently improved neocortical functioning. In many subjects at certain times, the hypnotic state produces neuromuscular changes implicating the old extrapyramidal system, simulating paralysis agitans without the tremors.* Clinical evidence of extrapyramidal involvement includes standing, sitting, moving, and turning in one piece; slow gait; loss of automatic associated movements; infrequent movements of natural expression, e.g., diminished blinking (eyelid catalepsy); flexion of neck, trunk and/or limbs; diminished swallowing reflex; delayed answering of questions; slow monotone speech often of lower pitch. To date, spontaneous, slow, undulating (athetoid) movements have been observed in two subjects, Fig. 2. At Yale Medical School in 1960, one of these subjects spontaneously developed camptocormia, a conversion symptom with forward bending of the back and head flexed at right angles to the back, Fig. 3. EMF measurements by Burr, who was as surprised at this development as the others, recorded a straight-line pattern indistinguishable from a hypnotic state. Another unusual extrapyramidal accompaniment of hypnosis was noted in one of the 1980 patients who developed pronounced jerky (choreiform) movements of her upper extremities, soon followed by participation of the lower extremities even when practicing autohypnosis at home alone. She correctly, but unwittingly, likened these movements to "St. Vitus' dance." Her hypnotic sessions were associated with marked improvement in her hot flashes and depressed state, as well as the removal of certain inhibitions—which she demonstrated by kicking off her shoes at the

* The production of momentary gross tremors of the hands and arms have thus far been noted in only one subject.

onset of these gyrations.

Incidentally, in both hypnotic subjects previously noted, the spontaneous athetoid movements developed only once as did the camptocormia in one of the athetoid subjects—the athetoid movements and the camptocormia having been manifested at different times and under different circumstances.

As another clinical manifestation linking hypnosis to the ancient brain core, the prolonged time it takes to develop an adequately deep hypnotic state for experimental work as well as psychomotor retardation suggests involvement of the slowly conducting internuncial neurons. Yet the fixed structural elements of the nervous system cannot explain field phenomena in their totality.

The Burr-Northrop *Theory* provides for the emergence of a definite nervous system, developing not from functional demands, but as a result of dynamic forces imposed on cell groups by the total field pattern. Field correlates of state changes provide for the "dynamo" functions of the ancient brain core—that of an intermediary agency for storing, mobilizing and directing energy which must reach a certain plateau before neocortical activity eventuates. The fixed structural elements of nervous organization give direction to transient, relatively stable but slowly changing, dynamic patterns of performance as a whole, which define the individual field. While operating through such structures, however, the polarized field is neither circumscribed to such regions nor inalterably associated with any specific arrangement of the nervous units. Thus, no model of the field can be constructed in terms of traditional mechanics, yet certain aspects of its intensity and polarity quantities can be measured peripherally and expressed in energy quanta.

Both emotional activity and stimuli of any kind involve mobilization of energy, as indicated on the millivoltmeter. Both emotions and stimuli evoke the same energy. *Emotions can now be equated with measurable energy.*

2

The beginning functioning of man's recently evolved neocortex provides new problems including those of trapped reverberating memories and programmed ideas. Field measurements highlight phylogenetically primitive energy interchanges, the basic state-function of the individual at any given time and hypnotic depth. But especially in hypnosis, memories and ideation are of utmost importance in *specific* ways as exemplified by theoretically predicting and experimentally demonstrating EEG correlates of hypnotically revivified seizures, detailed in Chapter 8. In this experiment, after the requisite hypnotic depth was obtained, the subject revivified previously experienced electroshock treatments with the identical disruptive EEG changes found with AC-induced convulsions, providing further evidence for the mechanical causal theory of trapped reverberating memories.

Later, paralleling this systematic experimental extension of field physics to biology, medicine and the behavior fields, in 1970, a unified tripartite logic for Psychology and Psychiatry was formalized mathematically by Fonseca, grounded in circular mechanical causal theory. As first suggested by Northrop in 1939, like field approaches, this logic extends the epistemology and scientific methods of math-physical entities to individual persons. From this, a neurophysiologic diagnostic and prescriptive psychiatry has evolved, including the logic of human intentions. To obtain a greater comprehension and eventual control of deviant human thinking and behavior, and to gain a more basic working knowledge of trance states, it will be necessary to explore fully the logical deductive consequences both of field and circular mechanical causal theories of man.

The superior discriminatory thinking which is often produced in hypnotic states may be due to the mobilizing, directing and focusing of the field energy from the ancient brain core upon neocortical tissue for improved performance and control. Yet before such phenomena can be effected, the variable baseline energy level must be changed to permit the subject to mobilize, direct and focus it for specific goals he wishes to achieve.

As demonstrated electrometrically, hypnotic states—which are intense states of concentration not necessarily dependent on any hypnotist and which can arise spontaneously—represent natural waking state changes involving (1) slow time-dependent field shifts in the balance of the ancient brain core to the phylogenetically recent neocortex in which field properties of the entire body participate and (2) mathematically formalized circular mechanical causal factors in human subjects. Following the requisite time for slowly changing field factors to undergo necessary alterations from nonhypnotic waking states, valid revivifications of specific past experiences then become possible—the same detailed memory revivifications obtained by Penfield through cortical electrostimulation.

3

In summary, the electromagnetic field-neurocybernetic theory (theoretic dynamic electromagnetic circular mechanical causal theory) of hypnotic states in comparate neuropsychologic persons has been developed, based on both electromagnetic field considerations and mathematically formalized circular mechanical causal factors. This is associated with the only known objective, quantitative, reproducible measurement of changing statefunction including hypnotic states, theoretically predicted and first experimentally demonstrated at Yale Medical School, 1948-1950.

Chapter Eight

TRAPPED REVERBERATING MEMORIES

1

Experiments of Schaefer (1960), Backus (1962), Stratus (1962) and Churchill (1964), suggested that seizures previously produced by electroshock treatments could be revivified by hypnosis. In that event, EEG tracings corresponding with these revivified seizures should confirm the validity of stored reverberating memories and also the slow-developing EMF changes as hypnosis deepens, which must precede true memory revivification. An experiment in 1962 confirmed that this is possible.

Our subject 724 had received electroshock treatments in June 1959, for the depressed component of his manic-depressive disorder. He did not suffer from epilepsy and had not previously experienced convulsions. On December 10, 1962, at age 39, he developed an auto-hypnotic state to revivify these shock treatments in the EEG Department, Norfolk General Hospital Division, Medical Center Hospitals under experimental conditions.

This EEG experiment was recorded on 16mm film by R. V. Fischbeck. The subject had received previous hypnotic training during which his EMF was monitored to determine the exact depth of hypnosis. One of Erickson's ideomotor induction techniques was taught: catalepsy of the right arm which, as hypnosis deepened, slowly repositioned itself downward from its original perpendicular position.

When the subject was ready for electroshock revivification, he signaled by extending his right index finger that the proper depth of hypnosis had been obtained. This was necessary because EMF monitoring was impractical during this experiment due to the technical complications of simultaneous EEG recording. The latter was made by unipolar right and left frontal, temporal, parietal and occipital leads.

Hypnotic induction was started at 4:15 p.m. with right arm catalepsy as in the training period, Fig. 11a. As hypnosis deepened, the arm slowly moved downward until the extension of the right finger signaled the proper depth, Fig. 11b. The EEG record showed low-voltage (<35μV) fast activity with occasional 10- to 12-cycle/sec low-voltage alpha rhythm. Much muscle artifact was also seen.

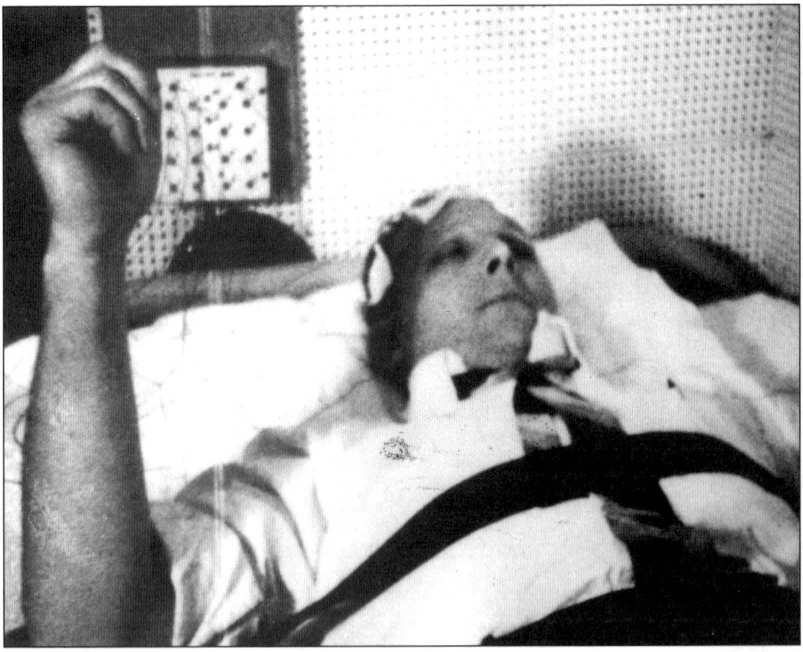

FIG. 11a. Hypnotic induction with right arm catalepsy, 724, EEG Department, Norfolk General Hospital Division, Medical Center Hospitals, Norfolk:, VA, December 10, 1962, 4:15 p.m.

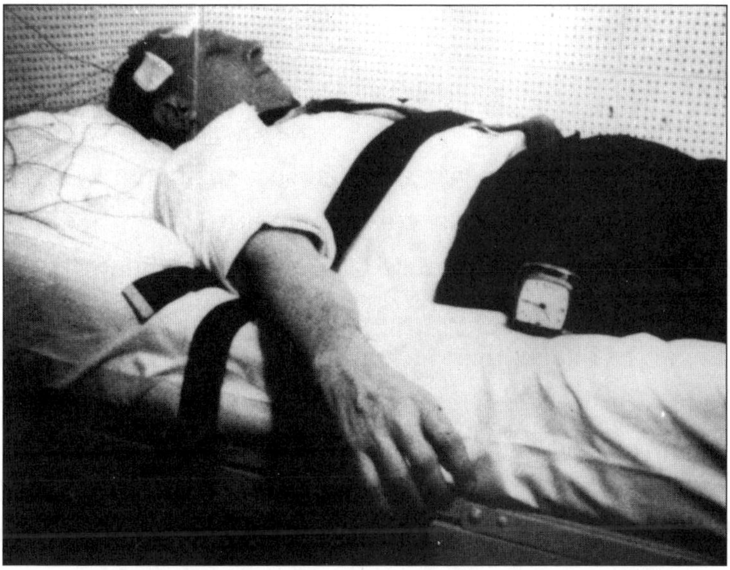

FIG. 11b. Right arm down and index finger beginning to extend, signaling attainment of proper hypnotic depth, 4:45 p.m.

The signal that the proper depth had been obtained was given at 4:45 p.m., indicating that the subject soon would be ready. At 5:01 p.m.—forty-six minutes after hypnotic induction—a camera flashbulb and shutter click were released. These were the stimuli to which the subject had previously been conditioned to trigger a convulsive episode.

During the initial training period, various hospital odors such as rubbing alcohol had been introduced to create a suitable "atmosphere" for the experiment. Lubricated teaspoons, simulating shock-electrode sensations, were held over right and left temporal areas. With increasing appreciation of the subject's capabilities, these props were eliminated during later experiments. A travel clock was placed next to the subject to record timing on the film and on color slides.

2

The first episode began with a tonic phase, followed in fourteen seconds by clonic activity. An isolated, poorly defined dome and spike complex was followed in seven seconds by a burst of slow activity. In five seconds an episode of slow 5-cycle/sec waves, including a few poorly organized spikes ensued, finally culminating in a gross pattern disorganization of moderate (35 to 75μv) and high (>75μv) voltage; then locked, fast 27- to 30-cycle/sec grand mal frequencies mixed with much muscle artifact, combined with slow 4- to 7- cycle/sec waves and some voltage asymmetry: left parietal lead > right parietal during the clinical clonic correlate. Return to nonconvulsive EEG pattern began twenty-four seconds later with the rocky baseline becoming increasingly stabilized and muscle artifact virtually disappearing.

During this experiment, five consecutive signals were given to the subject and the results recorded in the same way. These need not be repeated here. It is sufficient to say that each episode produced EEG seizure patterns except the fourth signal, given seven minutes, five seconds after the third. This was followed by a single spike, which in the left frontal lead achieved a poorly defined 0.5 second spike-and-dome formation, clinically correlating with a myoclonic jerk.

Fig. 11c shows typical revivified seizure sequence 3 (637) showing initial hi-voltage spike-and-dome response followed by brief restitution, then by onset of gross hi-voltage dysrhythmia correlating with clonic phase. Fig. 11d shows continuation of revivified seizure sequence 3 (638) indicating maintenance of dysrhythmia. Fig. 11e shows end of revivified seizure sequence 3 (639) illustrating restitution to preconvulsive EEG pattern.

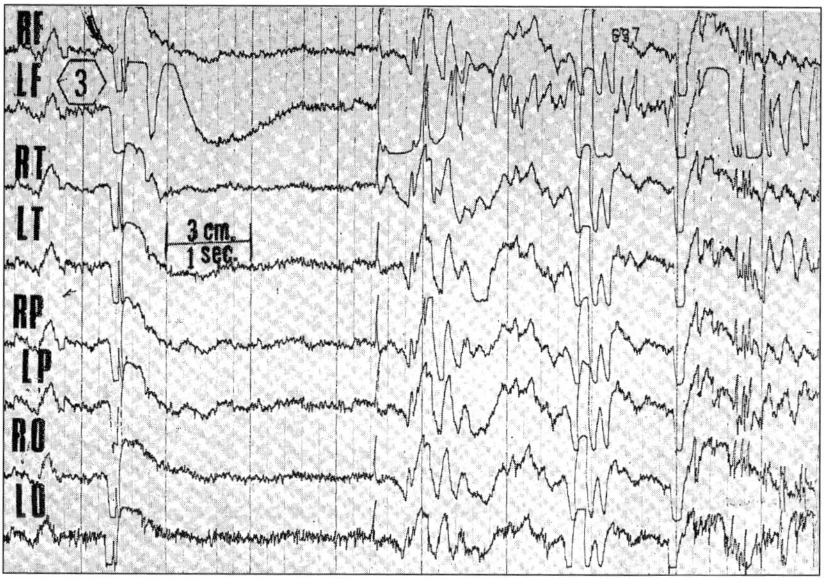

FIG. 11c. (read from bottom to top) Typical revivified seizure sequence 3 (637), showing initial hi-voltage spike-and-dome response followed by brief restitution, then by onset of gross hi-voltage dysrhythmia correlating with clonic phase. (Published in L. J. Ravitz: EEG correlates of hypnotically-revivified seizures. *J. Am. Soc. Psychosom. Dent. Med.* 29: 128-140, 1982.)

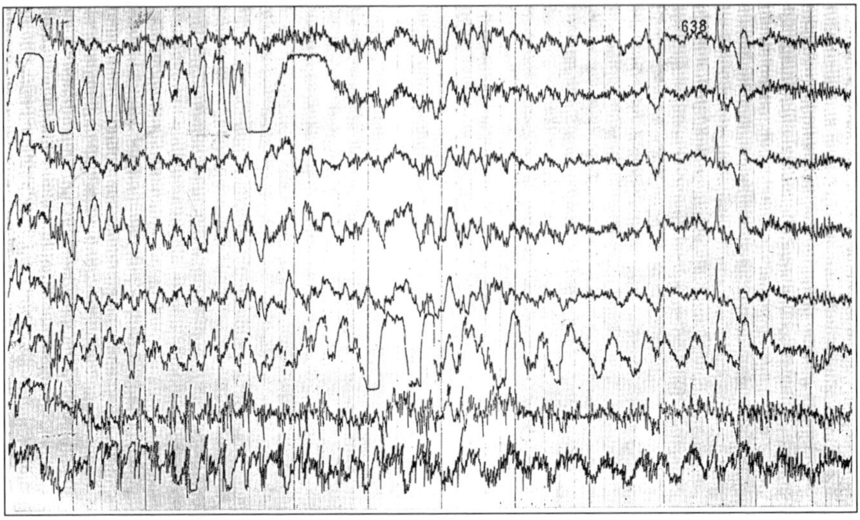

FIG. 11d. (read from bottom to top) Continuation of revivified seizure sequence 3 (638), showing maintenance of dysrhythmia. (Published in L. J. Ravitz: EEG correlates of hypnotically-revivified seizures. *J. Am. Soc. Psychosom. Dent. Med.* 29:128-140, 1982.)

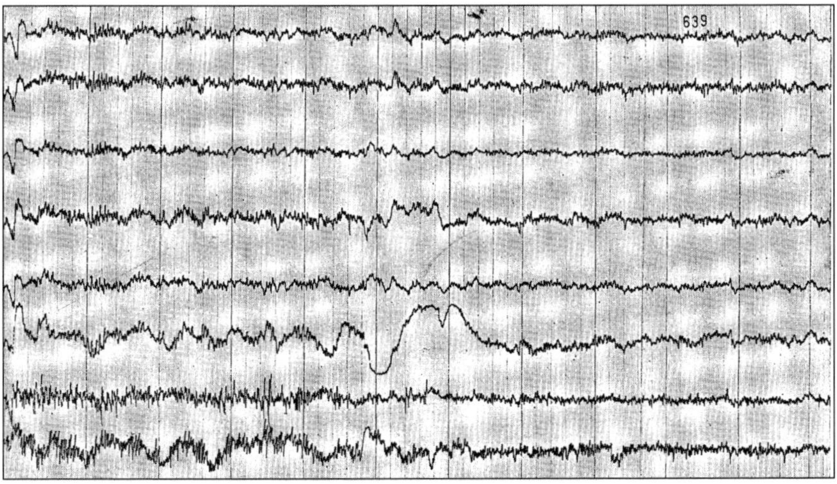

FIG. 11e. (read from bottom to top) End of revivified seizure sequence 3 (639), showing restitution. (Published in L. J. Ravitz: EEG correlates of hypnotically-revivified seizures. *J. Am. Soc. Psychosom. Dent. Med.* 29:128-140, 1982.)

At 5:15 p.m. unexpected visitors arrived and, perhaps detonated by some random sound, the EEG spontaneously developed mixed slow and fast frequencies combined with muscle artifact; asymmetries; and hi-voltage sharp, downward, spiky excursions tending to approach 6-cycle/sec psychomotor discharges, most pronounced in both parietal and the left occipital leads.

724, who was also amnesic for his previously experienced, externally produced grand mal seizures, could not explain this diagnostically significant episode but a misinterpreted signal from one of the spectators seemed the likely cause.

It is interesting to note that the subject did not experience any tongue biting, salivation, incontinence, fractures, muscle soreness or confusion which are so often associated with electroshock. Also, he experienced no subsequent grand mal seizures.

The EEG records were analyzed by Hallowell Davis, M.D., who

with A. J. Derbyshire, Ph.D. introduced Berger's EEG discovery into the United States at Harvard Medical School and Massachusetts General Hospital in 1934, and by F. G. Woodson, M.D., then the hospital electroencephalographer. They noted the characteristic seizure configurations, first described by Bagchi, Howell and Schmale in 1945, agreeing that they were typical.

When comparisons between hypnotically revivified and regular AC-induced seizures are made, EEG variations between individuals and within the same person at different times prevent clear-cut distinctions. Both produce disorganized EEG changes. The seizure discharges in this experiment would be rated *5* on a scale of *1* to *5* where *5* is diagnostically significant. (P. A. Davis 1941, Derbyshire and Ravitz 1958, summarized in Schwab 1951.)

3

Such experiments have important implications. They show that memories are not withered by age but remain as vivid as the day they originated throughout the life of the subject. Whether they are traumatic or harmless and pleasant, they continue to reverberate within us, even if we are not conscious of them.

As we have seen, they are powerful enough to produce the same EEG patterns and convulsions of externally applied electroshock.

These "internally" produced experimental hypnotic revivifications with demonstrable cortical changes provide findings similar to Penfield's "externally" (cortically) electrostimulated memory recall—furnishing further evidence for the theory of stored reverberating memories. Thus, whether actuated by externally applied AC current or by tapping trapped memories internally via hypnotic revivifications and their electromagnetic field correlates, the net EEG effect of such disparately produced grand mal seizures appears the same, further exemplifying the striking physiologic changes which can be effected by altering basic electric properties through hypnosis.

4

In a remarkable experiment, Erickson hypnotized a young man afflicted with acute myopia and regressed him to the age of eight—an age at which he had not needed glasses to read. Revivified memories of this period affected his eyes so that he was able to see signs from a distance and read books without glasses or eyestrain. This was not done as a cure nor to create permanent change in the eyes. It was just a brief experience in which the vision was somehow temporarily corrected.

It is clear that memories and emotions are a most important factor in the human organism—a force to be reckoned with. They can have a considerable influence on emotional and physical health.

Most of us have had evidence of the permanence of memory when some sight, sound or smell has revivified a memory which, until that moment, had long been "forgotten."

Revivification of memories by electric stimulation of the cortex has obvious difficulties and limitations. The skull must be opened and it seems to be a matter of pure chance which memories are revivified by the electrodes. Hypnosis has wider scope. It can regress the patient to early childhood when the child is first able to record memories and, in the process, revivify memories which may be relevant to the health of the patient.

It is both interesting and salutary to realize that many memories and emotions of a lifetime continue to reverberate below the level of awareness in all of us. Though they do not seem to affect well-balanced people, they may well account for some physical symptoms and emotional problems in others.

In the present state of our knowledge, the physician's only access to memories and emotions below the conscious level is by hypnotic regression.

Now the hypnotist has field measurements as a long-needed objective, quantitative, reproducible tool for use in his work. Obviously there is great scope and need for further research. As and when this is undertaken, it seems safe to say that the importance in medicine and Psychiatry of trapped reverberating memories will be increasingly recognized.

5

A striking example of the measurable effects of the emotion of fear was afforded by a secretary in her late forties at the Downey Veterans Administration Hospital in 1954. Subject 157 had a history of hemorrhaging peptic ulcer for which she was hospitalized in May 1953, and a lifelong phobia of birds. Her usual high intensity EMF tended to show minus polarity, with both severe physical symptoms and depression accompanied by unusually hi-minus patterns.

On May 20, 1954, she felt "quite well, if it wasn't for last night" and she guessed her reading would be *-20* mv. At 5:05 p.m., she actually read *-21* mv. At 5:10 p.m. Dolores, one of the parakeets who was also being monitored electrometrically, was brought into the office in a cage.

Within sixty seconds, the subject's EMF had accelerated to zero, reaching a maximum of *+50* mv by the end of the next minute— a two-minute increase of *+71* mv—and decelerated at a much slower rate being clocked at *+42* mv 30 seconds later. Face flushed, the subject jumped out of her chair and fled from the office. She adamantly refused to return, exclaiming down the hall that she was "scared to death."

Next day on May 21 at 4:48 p.m., her reading was *-13* mv with minimal variations. She felt well, guessed her last reading at *-21* mv, but investigated the writer's pockets to be sure Dolores was not hidden there. On the following Monday, May 24, at 4:54 p.m., she felt "unusually well—even better than Friday" and had "worked like a Trojan." Mixed polarity readings were recorded averaging *+3* mv.

Suddenly the voltages began to accelerate reaching a level of *+20* mv within one minute. Following a *+60* mv maximum during the next minute, they began to decelerate again at a slower rate. When asked what had happened, the subject replied that she had become fearful at the development of spontaneous thoughts of Dolores.

Shortly afterwards, on May 25, 1954, Subject 157 demonstrated that even an illusion can trigger voltage changes. She felt depressed and complained of dull back and front girdle pains which were reinforced by memories of hospitalization for hemorrhaging peptic ulcer, of which this was the anniversary. Her readings were now *-82* mv.

Suddenly at 5:02 p.m., her EMF again began accelerating in the plus direction with marked facial flushing. She exclaimed, "What is this? A shadow?" and was kept seated with difficulty. A *+38* mv maximum was recorded in about two minutes, representing a *+120 mv EMF shift;* again a slower decrease was noted. Ten minutes later, at a level of *+10* mv, the subject laughed spontaneously, saying that she had begun to feel fine and was symptom-free. All this happened because she had suddenly thought that she saw the shadow of Dolores the parakeet.

On June 1, 1954, one day after new moon and solar eclipse, Subject 157 measured *-103* mv at 4:05 p.m., the highest EMF recorded on her up to that time. "Only once or twice" had she ever felt as bad: "depressed, very tired, very weak, light-headed, faint and nauseated." She also was coughing and was very concerned over having noted a dark stool which she associated with her previous hemorrhaging ulcer, especially since abdominal cramps also were present and she felt that she couldn't cope with what was ahead of her.

That night she "slept like a log." The next afternoon, she registered *-80* mv, a 23 mv EMF detensification towards plus polarity in twenty-four hours. Though still depressed and "scarcely able to work," she no longer felt lightheaded and disclaimed abdominal cramps. Today, at least, she believed that she could cope with what was ahead.

Three caged parakeets were brought in: Dolores, Whitey and Greeney. Field measurements showed no change at all and the subject showed no sign of concern, stating that she did not feel well enough to care. From this it would seem that there exist intensities of discomfort at which one fails to respond even to a severe phobia.

Aside from illustrating dramatic field intensifications in the plus direction during (1) phobic reactions, (2) spontaneous emotive thoughts, and (3) response to an illusion, this case exemplifies field correlates of certain somatic symptom exacerbations and remissions. In addition, following a 120-mv shift with polar reversal, developed through misinterpreting a shadow as that of a bird, the subject, who had somatic symptoms prior to this event at hi-minus readings, became symptom-free ten minutes after her voltage peak, at a level in the low-plus range. Such improvement, however, did not endure, as the voltage level gradually returned to a hi-minus configuration.

Both emotional reactions and external stimuli evoke the same energy as read on the galvanometer which, with startle responses and fear reactions, have typically caused field intensifications in the plus direction. Emotions, as actuated through phylogenetically ancient brain centers, have thus been equated with EMF energy, sufficient intensification of which has been correlated not only with rigid, stereotyped, nondiscriminatory, nonintegrative thinking and behavior, but often with specific somatic symptoms and disorders when shifted in the minus direction. Other related studies suggest that reactivity to stress may be dependent largely on the position and momentum of the subject with respect to his electrocyclic pattern, a time-dependent variable which seems to be of crucial significance in the conditioning process. Such experiments have also indicated that following various kinds of stresses, especially psychologic, return to the original voltage level has been delayed up to an hour in certain persons, some of whom were diagnosed as being schizoid or schizophrenic. There seem to be intensities of somatic discomfort at which one fails to respond even to a severe phobia. In Subject 157, such "inertia" occurred during a period of similar field intensifications in other human subjects and parakeets being measured simultaneously, which also corresponded to a lunar syzygy in June.

It should be emphasized that the electrodynamic field is a unified organization and that abnormalities in one area affect the field as a whole. We can see, therefore, how fear—real or imaginary and whether consciously held or not—can have deleterious effects on the whole organism.

6

Trapped reverberating memories and emotions of the past, of course, are not the only ones to trigger field changes. Present anger or irritation can do the same, as has been demonstrated, and so can humor.

A pleasant episode was reported by a friend of mine who happened to be connected to a millivoltmeter when something hilarious occurred to him. Immediately his voltage reading increased by 10 mv, perhaps the first time in history that a humorous thought has been measured electrically.

In recent years, psychosomatic symptoms have gained increasing attention, and it is now generally recognized that such emotions as worry or anxiety may aggravate ulcers in those predisposed. Naturally, the emphasis has been on the effects of negative emotions. But perhaps more attention should be paid to the therapeutic effects of positive, optimistic emotions, especially now that it is possible to measure their effects on the field.

7

From the foregoing, it will be obvious that the ability to measure emotions—whether reverberating from the past or active in the present—opens up a wide field for further research. With the tool of electrometrics at his disposal, the psychologist or psychiatrist can tread more confidently in the tenuous and little explored jungle of human emotions and can more precisely assess their effects on physical and emotional health. This gives him a better chance to mitigate the pathologic consequences.

We have seen that an illusion can have a measurable effect on the field, as in the case of Subject 157 who thought she saw the shadow of a parakeet. Doctors and friends, therefore, should no longer dismiss as trivial the complaints of anyone because reported troubles "are all in the mind." Even an illusion can affect the field, and anything that can affect the field can affect the well-being of the organism as a whole.

For all of us, it is important to recognize some truth in the old saying that "thoughts are things" and to do what we can to govern our emotions.

If we cannot erase the trapped reverberating memory records of the past by conscious effort, we can at least be aware of their influence, shielding ourselves from the possible deleterious effects of the time-bombs of memory.

Chapter Nine

SCHIZOPHRENIC STATES AND THE FIELD

1

"Schizophrenic" is a term which often is used loosely and incorrectly—sometimes to describe some harmless eccentric or else someone we do not like! Though the cause is unknown, clinically diagnosed schizophrenic patients reveal voltage patterns ranging from the highest to the lowest intensities found. From adolescence to middle age, the greatest EMF strengths and variabilities, or *states of excitation,* are found in such disturbed persons despite their "front" and regardless of the apparent duration of their disorders. Clinical improvement is preceded, or accompanied by, sustained decreases in voltage intensity of greater stability and polarity may be reversed, i.e., the head electrode may change signs with respect to the reference electrode. The lowest field strengths and variability, or *states of exhaustion* usually are observed in chronic inert patients. Relatively rare disturbed behavior in this torpid group correlates with moderate field intensifications. The most dramatic voltage increases, usually of marked variability, have preceded those rare occasions when torpid schizophrenic behavior shifts into spontaneous animated functioning. Such intervals, which usually last from 12 to 48 hours, occurred only during periods of significant field intensifications in other life forms measured simultaneously. Since exaggerated or inhibited behavior may be found with high

EMF intensifications and as exhausted or torpid behavior accompanied by low readings may look like inhibited behavior, an EMF profile is necessary to indicate objectively what is going on and to provide an objective measure of the state of the patient. It follows then, that of two clinically similar mute schizophrenic patients inviting similar stock interpretations, one may be in a *state of excitation*, the other in a *state of exhaustion*.

To put it another way, the net effect of trying to start a car, either by flooding the carburetor or by not giving it enough gas, may be the same: in each case the car will not budge. To start the car requires knowledge of too much gas or too little.

Table 2 shows in linear time series one aspect of the field picture of schizophrenics and of nonpatient controls, indicating the significant differences between the mean field strengths of three matched groups: 34 disturbed schizophrenics, 34 chronic inert schizophrenics, and 34 controls. Most of the patients lived in a specific building as part of a controlled experiment designed to assess the efficacy of a rehabilitation program advanced by Paul Roland.

Table 3 not only indicates different field intensities during differently rated behavior states of the schizophrenics and during differently rated subjective feeling states in controls, but also illustrates the relative frequencies of disturbed, intermediate and optimal feelings in controls as well as disturbed, intermediate, inert or torpid and optimal behavior in the schizophrenic groups.

Only rarely within the twenty consecutive daily mean intensities used to compute these tables was the behavior of disturbed schizophrenics rated as anything but disturbed. Only rarely, too, was the behavior of the chronic inert schizophrenics anything but inert.

Significantly, ten of the chronic inert subjects returned to more optimal, animated, discriminatory and integrated functioning for about 3% of the time. During these transitory periods, their voltage levels approximated those of the disturbed group without any statistically significant differences, Tables 3 and 4.

Their disturbed behavior periods, likewise rare, tended to come in at voltage levels between the relatively optimal and those which characterized their typical torpid states. This study also bears out later observations which suggested that in such investigations, controls admit to feeling disturbed about one third of the time despite frequent dissimulation.

TABLE 2
DIFFERENCES BETWEEN MEAN FIELD INTENSITIES OF THREE SAMPLE GROUPS

Disturbed schizophrenics, chronic inert schizophrenics and controls: 2035 measurements of 102 subjects matched as to sex (male), general age and periods of measurement; computed by taking the mean of 20 consecutive daily mean voltage gradients for each subject.

Samples	No. of measurements	No. of subjects	**E** means (intensity)	S.D.	C.V.
			mv		
Disturbed schizophrenics*	675	34	46.3	24.9	54.1
Chronic inert schizophrenics †	680	34	12.4	5.2	43.3
Controls	680	34	16.2	6.8	42.5

*None diagnosed hebephrenic in hospital records.
† In hospital records, 56% diagnosed hebephrenic.

TABLE 3

DIFFERENCES BETWEEN MEAN FIELD INTENSITIES FOR BEHAVIOR STATUS OF SCHIZOPHRENICS AND FEELING STATES OF CONTROLS, TABLE 2

Samples	States	No. of measurements	%	No. of subjects	%	E means ( )	S.D.	C.V.
Disturbed schizophrenics*	Disturbed	594	88.0	34	100.0	49.6	23.6	47.2
	Intermediate	61	9.0	18	52.9	13.6	5.5	39.3
	Optimal	20	3.0	9	26.5	7.6	6.4	80.0
Chronic inert schizophrenics*	Disturbed	22	3.2	11	32.4	24.1	8.7	36.3
	Inert	641	94.3	34	100.0	10.8	4.7	42.7
	Optimal	17	2.5	10	29.4	56.1	22.7	40.5
Controls †	Disturbed	219	32.2	33	97.1	26.3	10.2	39.2
	Intermediate	179	26.3	34	100.0	14.1	9.3	66.4
	Optimal	282	41.5	32	94.1	9.1	5.1	56.7

*Behavior.

† Feelings.

TABLE 4
SIGNIFICANCES OF DIFFERENCES BETWEEN MEAN FIELD INTENSITIES, TABLES 2 AND 3

Comparisons	Difference*	C.R.	*P*
	mv		
Disturbed schizophrenics versus controls (TABLE 2)	30.1	6.8	<0.001
Chronic inert schizophrenics versus controls (TABLE 2)	3.8	2.6	<0.01
Disturbed schizophrenics verus chronic inert schizophrenics	33.9	7.8	<0.001
Disturbed schizophrenics versus optimal chronic inert schizophrenics (TABLE 3)	6.5	0.78	0.00

*Difference applies to mv means. (Tables 2, 3 and 4 published in L. J. Ravitz: History, measurement, and applicability of periodic changes in the electromagnetic field in health and disease. *An. NY Acad. Sc.* 98:1144-1201, 1962.)

2

As in all biologic systems, these values are relative; no magic number exists at which a person "becomes schizophrenic" or anything else. Of far greater significance are the degree and rate of field changes relative to the unique design of a given individual at a given instant. Although Table 4 indicates significant average intensity differences between groups, evidence accumulated since 1948 suggests that field variables may change from year to year. Certainly, seasonal and other cycles affect both polarity and intensity quantities in all groups. However, it seems likely that greater differences between, say, controls and disturbed schizophrenics appear during those cyclic periods of field strength intensification and vice versa.

Furthermore, in this study, significant differences existed between mean field strengths of controls and chronic inert schizophrenics. This tended to obscure the fact that individual field strengths of the chronic patients ranged from those far below any control to those significantly higher than the mean of the control group. Moreover, in such longitudinal studies, controls have become depressed or otherwise upset during the course of their measurements. Such state changes are, of course, reflected in their readings.

This indicates the inherent limitations of extended studies with linear orientations and rigidly tight compartments of controls versus any other group with which they are being compared.

Hence, in the final analysis, although disturbed schizophrenic groups have shown the highest field intensifies of any sample, and some disturbed schizophrenics likewise have shown the highest field strengths measured, what actually is of greater significance are degree and rate of voltage change relative to the unique configuration of a given organism at a given instant.

On the other hand, significant field strength differences between undisturbed controls and untreated, disturbed schizophrenics, whatever the general voltage level happens to be, already have pragmatic importance. For example, field measurements make it possible to unmask simulated schizophrenia, of which I encountered a striking case.

Subject 220, a 20-year-old woman admitted to the hospital for promiscuous behavior, had been diagnosed by her psychoanalyst as suffering from chronic schizophrenia. But despite her apparent disquietudes at experiencing frightening hallucinations, her sudden emotional outbursts and other grotesque behavior, her field measurements remained those of the most placid controls being monitored at the same time.

She had never previously been hospitalized for psychiatric reasons and prior to hospitalization had been fun-loving, carefree, boy-crazy and financially able to indulge her whims.

When Subject 220 met me in the hallways she would occasionally wink flirtatiously, whether or not she was in the middle of an emotional disturbance which kept much of the nursing staff in constant turmoil.

Finally, following some emotional tizzy during which her voltage gradients showed no significant variation, I informed her that, after all, I was not her psychoanalyst. The patient then asked the other personnel to leave the room and after they had done so, burst out laughing and admitted to me that she "had to do something for entertainment."

She confessed that she had been puzzled and envious of the fact that a schizophrenic patient who became a chum of hers always showed greater field strengths, so she had become proficient at simulating schizophrenic behavior by studying her friend. A few weeks later, apparently bored by this charade, she escaped from the hospital and was never returned.

She had succeeded in fooling her psychiatrist and the hospital staff but *she could not fool the millivoltmeter.*

This patient's field profile was that of an undisturbed control or a chronic inert schizophrenic patient. To be sure, she was diagnosed as suffering from chronic schizophrenia, yet I thought that her highly personable behavior failed to fit the diagnosis and her measurements were not those of a disturbed schizophrenic.

It might be added at this point that the field pictures of "psychopathic" or "sociopathic personalities" are those of undisturbed controls, unless or until they become disturbed. It is easy, therefore, to distinguish these from disturbed schizophrenics.

3

One of the most interesting and unusual cases studied by myself was that of identical (one-egg) twin brothers, age 26, both suffering from schizophrenia. EMF measurements of these twins, simultaneous with similar studies of other patients and hospital personnel, were started at the Veterans Administration Hospital, Salem, Virginia, in January 1951. Fig. 12 shows the five-day running averages of the twins, mean daily voltage gradients during different lunar phases from January to June 1951. Though similar, their periodic movements show notable differences.

From February through most of March, the EMF of twin A31 tended to decrease in positivity whereas that of twin B32 showed increasing positivity. Their highest readings occurred at approximately new or full moon.

During these phases A31 felt like preaching and became increasingly grandiose, paranoid, tense and irritable. Usually, too, he did not feel well physically, was less energetic during his highest EMF readings and mentioned that he felt badly. He also complained of sensations of "tightness" in the head and body.

On these occasions, he frequently argued with his twin, ranted about B32's "sinful" ambition to become a baseball player and urged him to become a preacher. He frequently exclaimed that he felt like "slaying the wicked."

During the first few months in which readings were taken, A31's EMF remained significantly higher than those of his twin, despite their downward trend. Throughout this period, A31 was sufficiently disturbed to require confinement while his twin was on ground privileges.

B32, on the other hand, was more receptive to his brother's suggestions during periods of highest voltage readings. At such times, he tended to accept and even be obsessed by his brother's delusions. His EMF spikes, too, were associated with feelings of apathy and depression and occasionally with mild hostility. He was less responsive to external stimuli and correspondingly less energetic and communicative, though he often talked to himself. He became increasingly preoccupied with religion, was unkempt, spent most of the time sitting inert and unresponsive and seemed more disturbed, disorganized and irritable.

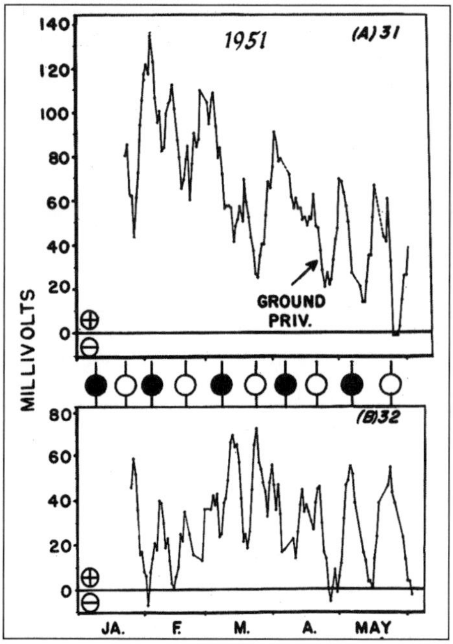

FIG. 12. Algebraic five-day running averages of the twins' mean daily voltage gradients during different lunar phases, VA Hospital, Salem, VA, January-June 1951. (Published in L. J. Ravitz: Comparative clinical and electrocyclic observations on twin brothers concordant as to schizophrenia, with periodic manifestations of *folie á deux* phenomena, *J. Nerv. Ment. Dis.* 121: 72-87, 1955.)

In B32, these exacerbated symptoms occurred more frequently in March than in any other month in which his EMF was plotted. He had been less withdrawn and preoccupied in February and showed signs of improvement from April until the experiment ended on June 15.

During spring, a general seasonal EMF decrease statistically significant beyond the .001 level—was observed in all patients including the twins. Table 5 illustrates arithmetic and algebraic calendar monthly means for A31 and B32 during the experiment. The greater the discrepancy between corresponding arithmetic and algebraic monthly means, the greater the polarity fluctuations—in this instance increasingly minus EMF during that month.

Though A31's highest EMF increases occurred in February, B32 did not reach his maximum until March. In these periods, plus polarity was more rigidly maintained. In June, however, both twins showed their lowest intensities, which were associated with observable changes.

A31 felt decidedly better and usually noted this spontaneously. His paranoid notions were less intrusive. He was calmer and more relaxed. He began to eat ravenously and felt less like preaching. As isolated low-intensity EMFs became more frequent during late winter and early spring, he continued to improve. By April 11, 1951, A31 had become noticeably fatter and on April 25 was granted ground privileges. Pressure of speech had all but vanished, and on April 26, he spontaneously admitted he felt much better than he had two months previously. He no longer worried about his brother not becoming a preacher and when the latter repeated his desire to become a baseball player, he merely shrugged his shoulders. By May 12, A31 had gained forty-four pounds since his EMFs were first read on January 23 and now weighed 226 pounds.

As B32's EMFs decreased, he became more responsive, active, gregarious and humorous. He took great delight in ribbing his twin about his religion and was less receptive to his ideas. During these intervals, B32 volunteered that he felt much better, often sang or hummed popular tunes and played baseball with the other patients. He was more particular about his appearance, often smoked a corncob pipe or affected a long cigarette holder, and seemed to enjoy life.

In both twins, it is interesting to note, as in all other subjects, the highest EMF spikes were often preceded or followed by unusually vivid dreams.

EMFs of both patients were significantly higher than those of undisturbed controls. The differences, therefore, in the voltage

TABLE 5
COMPARATIVE MEAN FIELD INTENSITIES AND POLARITIES OF SCHIZOPHRENIC TWIN BROTHERS

ARITHMETIC AND ALGEBRAIC CALENDAR MONTHLY MEANS, 1951												
SUBJECT	February		March		April		May		June		AVERAGE SYNODIC MONTHLY MEAN	
	E	H	E	H	E	H	E	H	E	H	E	H
(A)31	98.4	*+98.4*	65.4	*+63.8*	55.0	*+54.8*	41.4	*+37.2*	22.8	*+21.8*	56.5	*+55.2*
(B)32	31.2	*+17.6*	50.6	*+44.0*	35.2	*+28.0*	34.2	*+29.4*	10.8	*+6.4*	32.4	*+25.1*
← MILLIVOLTS →	CORRESPONDING SYNODIC MONTHLY MEANS*											
	Jan. 22 – Feb. 21		Feb. 21 – Mar. 23		Mar. 23 – Apr. 21		Apr. 21 – May 23		May 21 – Jun. 19		AVERAGE SYNODIC MONTHLY MEAN	
	E	H	E	H	E	H	E	H	E	H	E	H
(A)31	93.0	*+91.8*	75.2	*+74.0*	57.2	*+56.4*	40.8	*+39.0*	28.6	*+25.6*	58.9	*+57.4*
(B)32	32.8	*+22.2*	46.8	*+37.6*	43.6	*+40.8*	30.4	*+21.2*	21.8	*+18.6*	35.1	*+28.1*

* As field measurements began and ended with the phase of full moon, lunations are calculated from this reference point. (Published in L. J. Ravitz: Comparative clinical and electrocyclic observations on twin brothers concordant as to schizophrena, with periodic manifestations of *folie á deux* phenomena, *J. Nerv. Ment. Dis.* 121: 72-87, 1955.)

intensities of the twins could not only be attributed to their personality differences and contrasting behavior but also to regular, cyclic exacerbations of their symptoms—virtually independent of situational provocation.

Though acute emotional disturbances can precipitate dramatic EMF intensities apart from the expected EMF variations, these studies indicate that such disturbances often represent far more than a simple response to the immediate situation. Had the twins been undergoing psychotherapy at the time, their improvement might have been attributed only to subjectively perceived factors.

This immediately questions the often glib interpretations of clinical changes in patients undergoing treatment, whose improvement may sometimes depend far more on variables not connected with therapy than has hitherto been suspected.

4

To summarize this unusual case, a pair of schizophrenic identical male twins was studied over a five-month period. The study involved daily EMF readings taken simultaneously on other patients and hospital personnel to compare EMF variations of the twins with those of the control group. Independent clinical observations of daily fluctuations in mood and behavior were also recorded over the same period and compared with EMF shifts.

Until his symptoms improved, the more disturbed twin showed much higher EMFs than did his brother. However, daily EMF readings of both revealed similar rhythmic variations. The magnitude of these could be related not only to their contrasting behavior and disturbances but also to regular periodic exacerbations of their psychotic symptoms.

The symptoms of the less disturbed twin may have been enhanced by the occasional influence of his actively delusional brother. Beyond that, however, it would be speculative to assume that the symptoms of the twin partners might have been entirely different or might not have developed at all if they had not been reared together.

5

Earlier it was stated that variations or deviations in the field often precede physical events such as ovulation or malignancy. The following examples show that the same thing happens in the case of emotional disturbances.

A Duke University student, age twenty-four, Subject A75, who had been enlisted as one of the controls, showed intensities and diurnal, daily and fortnightly variability that greatly exceeded those of any control being monitored at the same time. In fact, they paralleled the field profiles of disturbed schizophrenic patients. Figs. 13a and 13b show, respectively, his five-day running averages and day-to-day graph of mean field excursions.

Though somewhat shy and sensitive, A75 was a personable young man and showed no remarkable symptoms or signs beyond ordinary perturbations at various times. However, on August 6, 1952, one day after new moon, his mean field measurements read *+121* mv, at that time the highest ever recorded on any control subject. Questioned, he revealed he had awakened within the preceding hour to hear his pillow breathing, and in a panic had stuck his hand into a small bedside fan, fortunately without serious injury.

His general ideation was such that he was referred to a consulting psychiatrist who thought that this represented a schizophrenic episode, a diagnosis further suggested by psychologic tests and by a third psychiatrist at a later date.

It is important to note that the field profile suggested a profound disturbance long before any significant clinical evidence came to light—a striking example of the ability of field measurements to predict future states.

Diminished EMF intensifications and variability which naturally accompany aging may account for more improvements, with or without treatment, than has generally been accepted. By the same token, subtle signs of deterioration, which often occur after acute schizophrenic episodes and which may coexist with "overall improvement," now have a physiologic rationale based on relative *states of exhaustion.*

Another case studied was that of Subject 103, a low-voltage chronic torpid schizophrenic patient. He had rare observable clinical changes which correlated with sudden, brief EMF intensifications of greater variability.

The 16 mm sequences in Fig. 14A-H are pictures of Subject 103 which were filmed by Ted Maciejewski, Downey Veterans Administration Hospital, North Chicago, Illinois, in the spring and summer of 1954. During this period, average EMF intensity for the chronic torpid group (in *states of exhaustion*) was 12 mv, significantly less than that of the control group averaging 16 mv and the disturbed schizophrenic group (in *states of excitation*) averaging 46 mv, Table 2.

Usually, Subject 103 was mute. He ritualistically filled his shoes, pants and jacket with unread newspapers, torn magazines, paper scraps, cloth, string and twigs. He also stored such trash between his teeth. Usually, he stared with a fixed facial expression. "...a pack rat, vegetating, empty..." At relatively rare moderatel high field intensifications, averaging 24 to 40 mv, though still mute, unresponsive and with a mask-like countenance, he appeared confused and resisted any attempts to move him or to remove his shirt for measurements.

However, the most exaggerated field intensifications, usually of marked variability and tending to approximate lunar syzygies, preceded those very rare periodic occasions when torpid behavior changed to animated spontaneous functioning. Such brief episodes, averaging twelve to twenty-four hours or less, occurred during periods of the same significant field intensifications in other simultaneously measured patients, controls and parakeets.

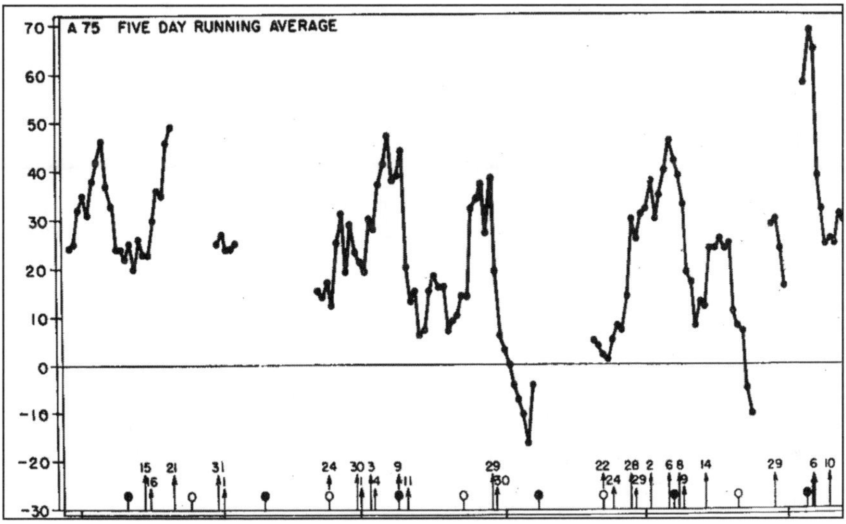

FIG. no. 13a. Algebraic five-day running average of mean daily field measurements of control Subject A75, whose disorganized state became manifest in early August 1952 following hi-plus intensifications at full moon, Duke Medical School. • = full moon, o = new moon (Published in L. J. Ravitz: History, measurement, and applicability of periodic changes in the electromagnetic field in health and disease. *An. NY Acad. Sc.* 98: 1144-1201, 1962.)

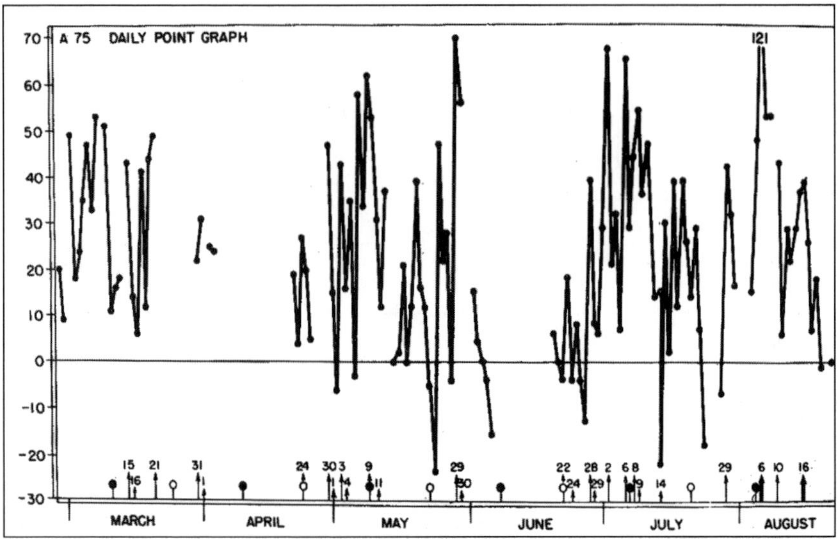

FIG. 13b. Algebraic mean daily field measurements of Subject A75, showing marked field-strength variability in a control more typical of a disturbed schizophrenic patient. • = full moon, o = new moon (Published in L. S. Ravitz: History, measurement, and applicability of periodic changes in the electromagnetic field in health and disease. *An NY Acad. Sc.* 98: 1144-1201, 1962.)

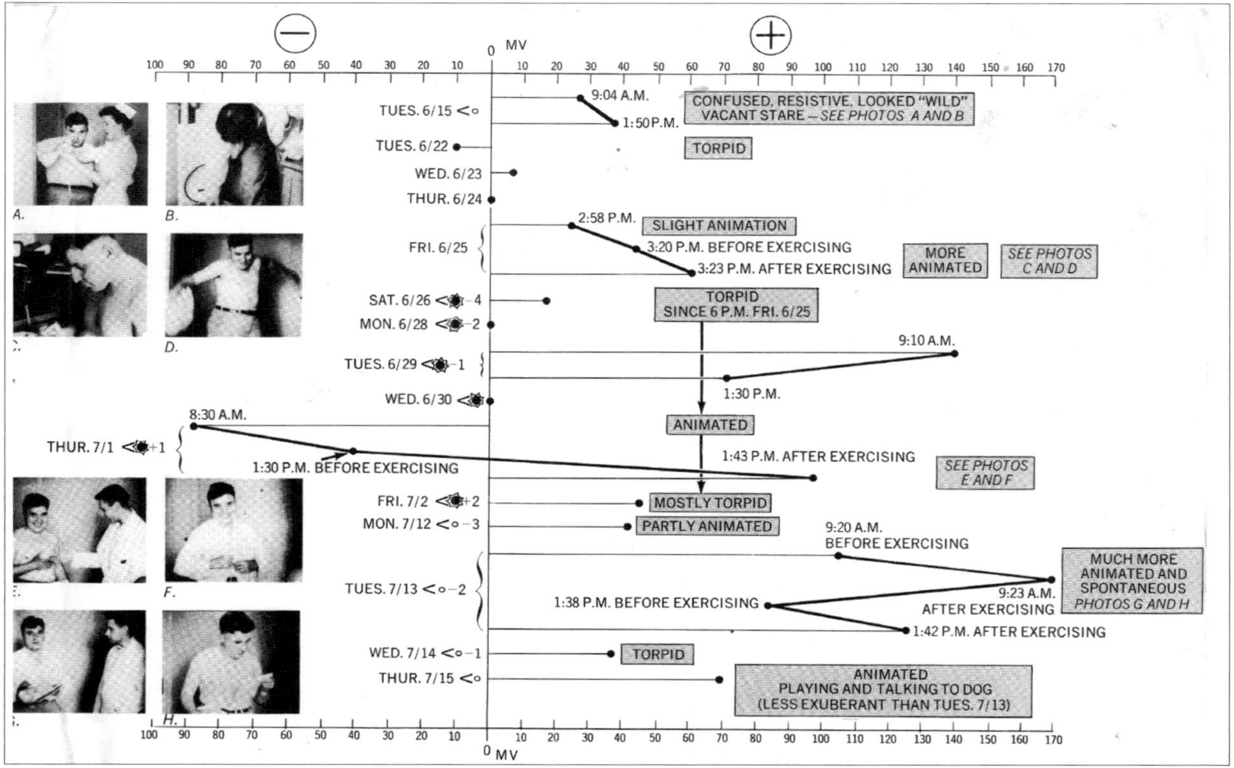

FIG. 14. Corresponding photos and voltage gradients of chronic schizophrenic patient (103) during different states: (A & B) confused, resistive; (C) more animated; (D) exercising; (E & F) more animated after exercising; (G & H) much more animated and spontaneous after exercising. Downey VA Hospital, N. Chicago, IL, 1954.

Another patient, A71, a male Duke University student, age nineteen, had undergone electroshock and insulin subshock treatments in January 1952. Fig. 15 illustrates his five-day running average of mean daily field measurements. Severe symptoms tended to coincide with lunar syzygies, especially new moon.

Following his return to school in September, sharp downward EMF excursions with a minus polar reversal *preceded* the development of a moderately severe respiratory infection, Fig. 15.

In subject A71, such hi-minus field intensifications were not associated with depersonalization, withdrawal and other symptoms that customarily characterized his hi-plus states.

Though obviously there is great scope for further research, the cases described in this chapter show that field measurements are a reliable, indispensable tool for the diagnosis and treatment of the psychiatrically disturbed.

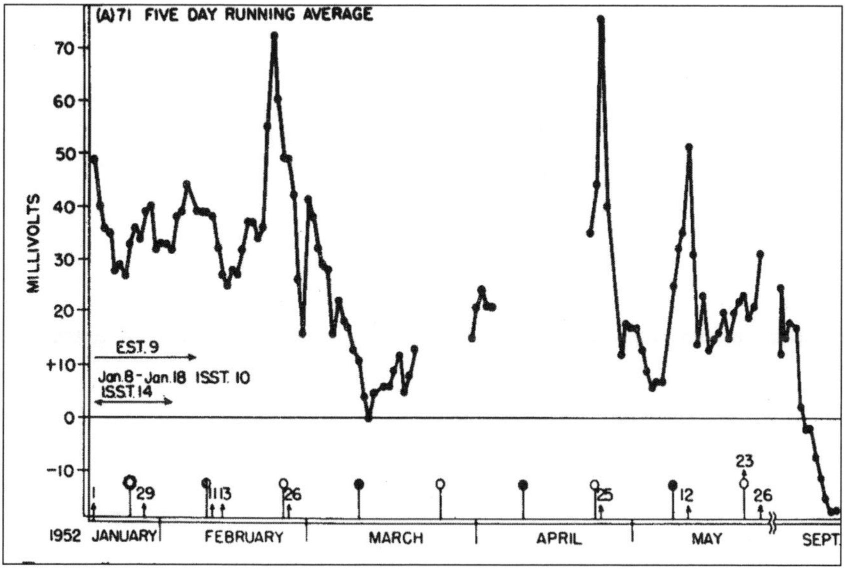

FIG. 15. Algebraic five-day running average of mean daily field measurements of depersonalized patient A71, who initially received combined electroshock and insulin subshock treatments; showing characteristic winter field-strength intensifications of plus polarity in a disturbed schizophrenic patient followed by diminished excursions and subsequent improvement during seasonal voltage detensifications (especially at full moon in March 1952), symptom exacerbations and remissions during certain lunar phases and development of upper respiratory infection following minus polar reversal of hi intensification in September, Duke Medical School. • = full moon, o = new moon (Published in L. J. Ravitz: History, measurement, and applicability of periodic changes in the electromagnetic field in health and disease. *An. NY Acad. Sc.* 98: 1144-1201, 1962.)

Chapter Ten

Manic-Depressive States* and the Field

1

Since true manic-depressive psychoses tend to occur later in life than schizophrenic states, it follows that the voltage excursions during perturbations in statefunction would generally be less than those seen in younger age groups and of more predominantly negative polarity. To be sure, involutional depressions and manic-depressive psychoses in either phase have been correlated with predominantly positive excursions in subjects beyond fifty years of age. However, as might be expected, another important determinant of polarity appears to be electrocyclic phenomena, and hence the season at which the manic or depressive episode becomes apparent as well as the fortnightly and diurnal timing of various symptoms and signs. As voltage measurements vary with the individual, one manic-depressive patient may become manic during the northern hemisphere spring-summer hi-minus EMF swings and be depressed in the hi-plus winter phase whereas another becomes manic during the winter hi-plus polarity excursions. Yet individual polarities at which manic and depressive states become manifest have remained constant for individuals within general age groups.

Like state perturbations in other forms of life, manic and depressive episodes are preceded by or correlated with field intensifications as a rule. Hence, so far as field quantities are concerned, a manic state represents a *state of excitation*, as do most depressive states seen thus far. This finding is more readily comprehended

* The American Psychiatric Association currently classifies Manic-Depressive States as Bipolar Disorders.

when one considers that *states of excitation* can cause facilitation or inhibition of response as exemplified by pronounced field strengths in acutely disturbed catatonic schizophrenics irrespective of phase. Diurnal rhythms are especially pronounced in these conditions or in instances showing relatively contracted diurnal variations and the patient tends to manifest disquietudes at even the least field intensification and variability, i.e., a lower threshold appears to be present. The time of the day that the most pronounced shifts occur tends to be the period when the patient feels worst. In those cases showing exacerbations both in the morning and in the evening, relatively high excursions are present at both times of day, typically of one polarity in the morning and the opposite polarity in the late afternoon and early evening. Such **H** quantities have no necessary relationship to manic or depressive phases, however. A person may become manic or depressed at intensifications in either direction. Yet in those persons who tend to have an alternating seasonal cycle of manic and depressive states, excursions in one direction have been noted in one phase and intensifications in the other direction have been measured in the opposite phase. Although this is highly individuated, a mania occurring in early winter would tend to show field strength intensifications of plus polarity, and a depression in the late winter or spring would tend to manifest minus intensifications, relatively speaking. Likewise an early winter depression would characteristically show hi-plus intensifications, and a late winter or spring mania would tend to have hi-minus excursions. Moreover, the agitation or anxiety frequently accompanying depressions can now be understood in terms of basic field strength intensification, whatever the direction.

The pronounced somatic symptoms often associated with involutional depressions but which occur in other clinical forms of depression and in schizophrenia as well, have to date been seen only in subjects showing hi-minus intensifications, illustrating the importance of the **H** quantity with somatic distress irrespective of clinical diagnosis. In this connection, no distinguishing features earmark the field profiles of manic-depressive states as compared with other diagnosed forms of depression. Although an extraordinarily useful, predictive clinical adjunct, voltage gradients can scarcely serve as a substitute for astute clinical observations and discriminations. On the other hand, empirically derived clinical diagnoses require objective supplementation at the very least.

In only one instance thus far has a *state of relative exhaustion* been seen in a patient who was then thought to be depressed. Subject 219, a twenty-four-year-old woman, whose average optimal state was always on the hypomanic side, developed a recurrent manic episode in the summer of 1955, which by fits and starts reached its peak in November and December, both clinically and electrically. As her hi-plus voltage gradients began to decrease toward the end of December, she became friendlier and more cooperative. However, by mid-April and the first week of May 1956, her field intensities hovered around zero with minimal day-to-day and diurnal variations. Although she appeared neat and remained cooperative and cheerful, she was thought to be clinically depressed by her physician. She felt "like a vegetable" and could not concentrate on reading material. On May 9, electroshock treatments were begun by her psychiatrist. Following this, her field intensities surged upwards to some extent and by the fourth treatment she was in a mild manic state. In accord with the seasonal field decrements in all other subjects, her relatively hi-plus excursions soon subsided, and she was discharged on June 1.

The case of Subject B77 illustrates another type of manic-depressive psychosis in a woman, age forty-two, and is included to provide a note on premenstrual tension states as well as factors promoting "recovery" (Figs. 16a and 16b). Her greatest state perturbations tended to approximate lunar syzygies. Premenstrual tension symptoms began one day before new moon on May 22, and extended into her period, ending on June 1, an interval of considerable voltage flux. None preceded her menstrual period on June 20-22 during a period of low field intensities and minimal variability. Following the menstrual period, depressive-tension symptoms began to develop, reaching their maximum on June 25, three days after new moon, associated with pronounced field intensification in the plus direction. The tension component then dropped out, with augmentation of the depressive features. During the following negative excursion, she was thought to be suicidal on June 27. A short-lived depressive-tension state preceded the July menstrual period during intensifications in the minus direction.

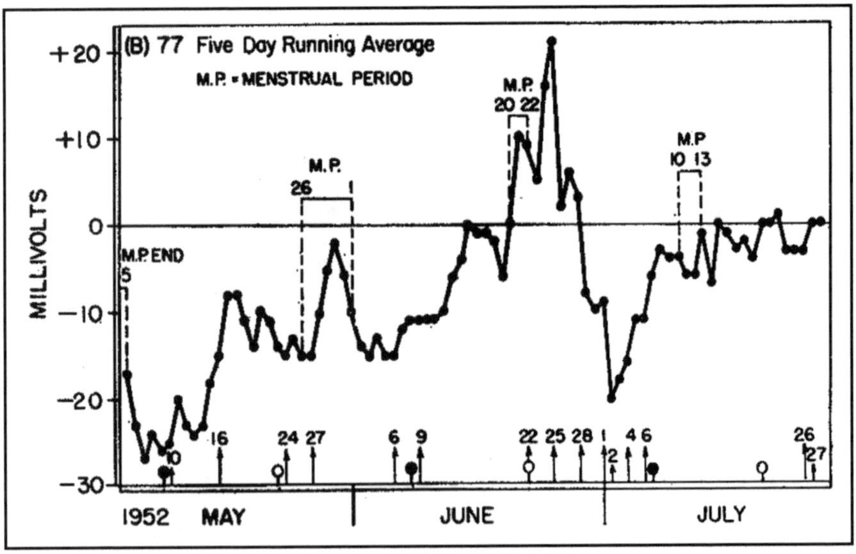

FIG. 16a. Algebraic five-day running average of mean daily field measurements of manic-depressive patient B77, showing diminished field-strength intensifications and subsequent improvement toward the end of July, Duke Medical School. • = full moon, o = new moon (Published in L. S. Ravitz: History, measurement, and applicability of periodic changes in the electromagnetic field in health and disease. *An. NY Acad. Sc.* 98: 1144-1201, 1962.)

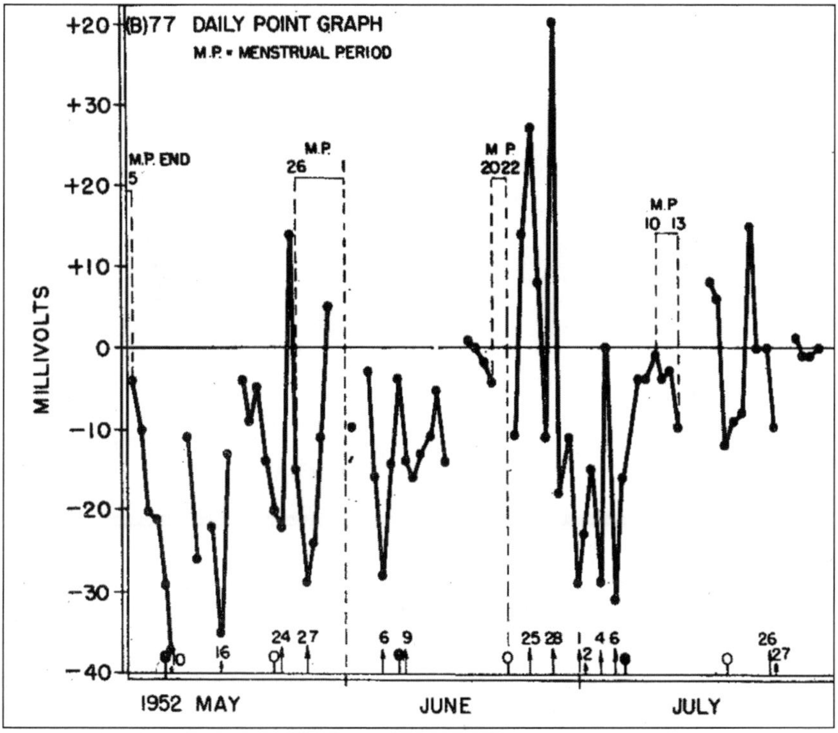

FIG. 16b. Mean daily field measurements of patient B77, showing moderate field-strength variability and menstrual periods. • = full moon, o = new moon (Published in L. J. Ravitz: History, measurement, and applicability of periodic changes in the electromagnetic field in health and disease. An. *NY Acad. Sc.* 98: 1144-1201, 1962.)

Her first psychoanalytic session began on May 28. She was thought sufficiently improved to warrant discharge from the hospital on July 31, to continue her psychoanalytic sessions on an outpatient basis. Voltage intensities were contracted in Subject B77 as they were in all subjects. In Fig. 17, similar excursions can be seen in Subject B81, a four-year-old boy supposedly suffering from childhood schizophrenia, who also improved sufficiently in certain spheres to be discharged from the hospital toward the end of August, again corresponding with a general period of lowered field-strength intensifications of contracted variability.

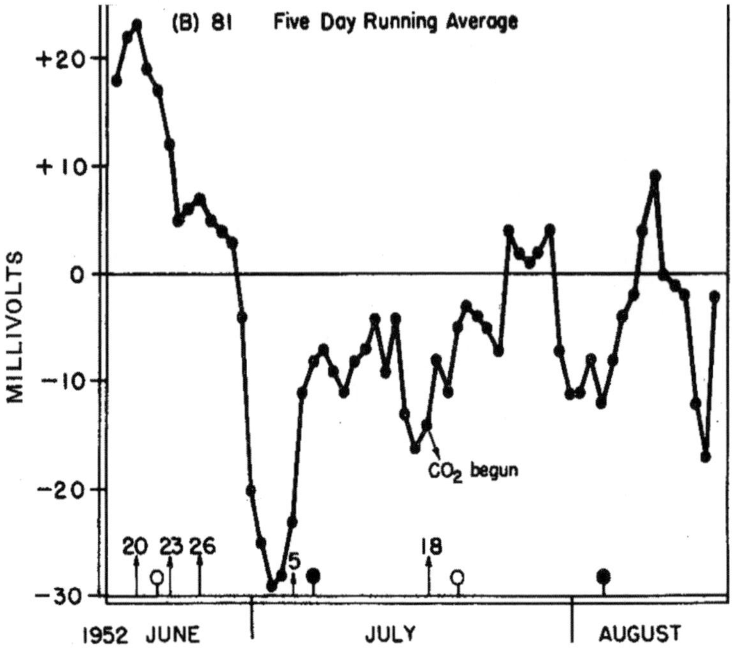

FIG. 17. Algebraic five-day running average of mean daily field measurements of "childhood schizophrenic" patient B81, showing phase correlations with patient B77 (Fig. 16a) as well as diminished field-strength intensifications and subsequent improvement toward the end of July. Duke Medical School. • = full moon, o = new moon (Published in L. J. Ravitz: History, measurement, and applicability of periodic changes in the electromagnetic field in health and disease. *An. NY Acad. Sc.* 98: 1144-1201, 1962.)

2

Improvement in patients undergoing some form of treatment is traditionally grounded to rigid preconceptions as to how a given empiric operational procedure achieves such favorable results. These are, in turn, based on the tacit belief that being a special creation, man is in the Universe but not of it—and beyond natural laws. Such notions exalt the omnipotence of any circumscribed methodology from pink pills to medical treatments and even the dogma of many contemporary religions. In psychiatry, e.g., glib pontifications are rampant concerning "deep" (that is, psychoanalytic or quasipsychoanalytic) versus "superficial" (that is, anything else) "psychotherapy." Yet, as Erickson has pointed out, in any therapeutic regimen, however well planned, there are always questions as to what constitutes adequate procedures, what alterations will come about and how and what the techniques used to achieve the results will mean in the total experiential life of the patient. Hence, it is pretentious to claim that in any form of empiric treatment fused to any empiric theory, one can account entirely for the results. The physician may know what he attempted to do, but he would scarcely know all of the ineffable experiential significances thereof to the patient, whose reactions are also conditioned by the concomitant impingement of other variables.

Notions of periodicities in clinical conditions, which have gone in and out of fashion through the centuries, can now be understood in terms of electrocyclic phenomena. Thus, the field variations in subjects B77 and B81 show almost identical phase correlations, also similar to the field patterns of other subjects who were measured simultaneously. Moreover, despite a complaint of premenstrual tension states, such symptoms preceded only two of subject B77's menstrual periods during the time of her measurements, being associated with periodic voltage increments of increased variability. On the other hand, symptoms which she associated with premenstrual tension states occurred during and even after menstruation during periods of field-strength intensification of heightened variability. This shifting "premenstrual" symptom complex also has been observed in other female subjects, suggesting that comparable states may be detonated only when there exists a concatenation of interrelated factors of sufficient magnitude, all pulling together. Further, in the diminution or absence of requisite forces causing periodic voltage increments, such symptoms may be reduced or shifted to periods in which high variable voltage gradients occur, or may even be absent. In any event, very little evidence exists to suggest the inference that any form of empiric treatment provided the crucial factor causing symptom improvement in subjects B77 or B81. Moreover, subject B77 again suffered from similar symptoms at expected periods of voltage variability during the latter part of 1952 and in the late spring and early summer of 1953. She was rehospitalized with the same clinical picture in the late spring of 1954, exactly two years following her first hospitalization.

Chapter Eleven

The Posited Phylogenetic Basis of Behavior Disorders*

Although numerous studies of so-called schizophrenic states suggest an involvement of the entire organism, examination of the central nervous system of such persons has failed to disclose any specific pathologic conditions or deviations that might not be accounted for on other grounds. In fact, prior to electromagnetic field experiments, only one known scientific investigation had suggested innate periodicities within the schizophrenic groups as being related to any other periodic movements. Gjessing was able to correlate rhythmic changes in nitrogen balance with certain catatonic reactions which he classified in accord with state changes of nitrogen excretion or retention.

In the nervous system, ontogenetically and phylogenetically, structure precedes function by a considerable lapse of time. There is reason to believe, moreover, that evolution is not only still progressing, but also that it proceeds at an uneven pace. With the emergence of increasingly differentiated forms of life, behavior has become less stereotyped and rigid, more modifiable and educable, until in man, the discriminatory and integrative neocortical controls assert their functional potentialities. As primitive responses are directly related to the autonomy of phylogenetically old centers, which under such intense affects as fear, rage, hate, jealousy, or profound sexual excitation, suspend and completely dispossess neocortical processes of education, culture, reason, judgment, memory and imagination, along with digestion, it is not surprising that all human reactions of this type reveal muscular tenseness and stereotyped rigidity. Such

*Presented at the New York Academy of Sciences International Conference Banquet, November 10, 1961.

attributes are not only increasingly characteristic of behavior as one descends the phylogenetic tree, but also are present to varying degrees in many schizophrenics in whom these might primarily represent not only an anthropocentric defense mechanism to the imperfections of life, but also their most natural ways of responding. Such phylogenetically primitive perturbations, moreover, have been correlated with field intensifications of great variability, which characterize all acutely disturbed behavior disorders.

In 1956, at the 112th annual meeting of the American Psychiatric Association, the phylogenetic basis of behavior disorders was presented. This construct derived from considerations of fundamental behavior changes at each step in the evolution of the nervous system with particular emphasis on the balance between ancient subcortical brain centers and neocortex, and the relationship of field intensification and variability to the suspension or disruption of the discriminatory, regulatory, integrative aspects of neocortical function. In brief, behavior disorders seem related to the innate degree of lability, loss or lack of integrative functioning between morphologically developed old and new nervous structures based on individual variations in the evolutionary functional maturity of neocortical tissue with respect to corresponding variations in the functional dominance or autonomy of the ancient components. Results of relatively intense field bombardment of relatively fragile neocortical tissue have been posited as follows: *states of relatively sustained excitation* with facilitation and/or inhibition of response; *states of periodic excitation* alternating with return to more optimal state-function and *states of reversible exhaustion*; *states of less reversible exhaustion* alternating with increasingly rare returns to *states of excitation* and relatively optimal statefunction and finally, in some, before the "flame" dies down, compensatory, periodic *states of excitation* at which optimal statefunction now occurs, alternating with *states of exhaustion,* followed by *relatively irreversible states of exhaustion.*

On the other hand, some schizophrenics may come equipped with a "defective dynamo," or such functionally deficient neocortical regulatory-integrative mechanisms that they would show gross symptoms in infancy and childhood—intellectual, discriminatory functions never developing, developing slowly or becoming arrested at an early age.

By this theory, the essential distinction between manic-depressive states and so-called psychoneurotic states and schizophrenia would be the more completely evolved, more functionally mature aspects of neocortical function in the nonschizophrenic behavior disorders. All, however, would progress through spacetime on electrocyclic variations conditioning state changes ranging from *excitation* to *exhaustion.* Moreover, all manics and most depressives would physiologically represent *states of excitation*—in one, with facilitation of response and in the other, with inhibition of response. Aside from the aged, the major group which would tend to succumb to *relatively irreversible states of exhaustion* would be the schizophrenic.

It follows that schizophrenic states, essentially comprising too little and/or too much of the natural responses to the internal and external environment, resulting in "wrong" reactions, represent neither a disease, nor the behavior of a "weak," "aberrant," or "pathologic ego." As phylogeny, like ontogeny, appears to be directed in an orderly fashion, although by fits and starts, such states may merely reflect incompletely although—in instances of superior intelligence—lopsidedly evolved organisms. All behavior disorders not conditioned by culturally false conceptions of "normal," reflect, by this construct, an imbalance in the harmonious integration of ancient brain centers and neocortex.

In one of the most striking accounts of "insanity without...intellectual delusions," Brenten called attention to the frequently neglected fact that apparently similar states may derive from opposite causes:

> Silence may proceed from irresolution or resolution, just as stillness may be the result of exhaustion, or of equally contending powers.

Hence, of two clinically indistinguishable, mute catatonic patients at any given time, one may be in a *state of excitation*, the other in a *state of exhaustion*. A voltmeter is needed to ascertain the statefunction of a car battery. Similarly, it is now postulated that a voltmeter is just as necessary for determining the statefunction of any living system, and appears to be particularly important in schizophrenic states. For example, somatic treatments eventually may cause diminutions of high voltage excursions. Thus, in a patient whose more optimal functioning appears to correspond only with higher, more variable field quantities than he ordinarily shows, such methods of treatment may not only fail to produce a desired clinical effect of any duration, but may eventually promote an irreversible *state of exhaustion*.

Chapter Twelve

THE ELECTRIC TIDES OF LIFE

1

Burr's interest in my preliminary 1948 experiments sparked the first longitudinal study of periodic movements or cycles in the human field. I had already noted spontaneously occurring changes in the field patterns of the same subjects at different times, whether they were prehypnotic, hypnotic or posthypnotic.

Over the 1949-1950 school year, therefore, I took daily and diurnal field measurements of Yale friends. As expected, the same electrocyclic phenomena were recorded which Burr had previously found in other life forms, including trees. Burr had studied human cycles only in the case of female menstrual cycles. So I decided to study the cycles of both males and females, and an initial report of my discovery was first published in the *Yale Journal of Biology and Medicine* in September, 1951. In the course of this study, somatic disorders as well as emotional perturbations were monitored, and the first somatic and emotional correlates were established. Within a 12-month span, the most notable periodic movements were diurnal, fortnightly—approximating new and full moon—and seasonal. Figs. 18-20 show algebraic five-day running averages of mean daily field measurements during different moon phases, Yale Medical School, 1949-1950. Fig. 21 denotes algebraic finger potential plots for one male and three females, showing presumed ovulation time (indicated by arrows) and menstrual periods.

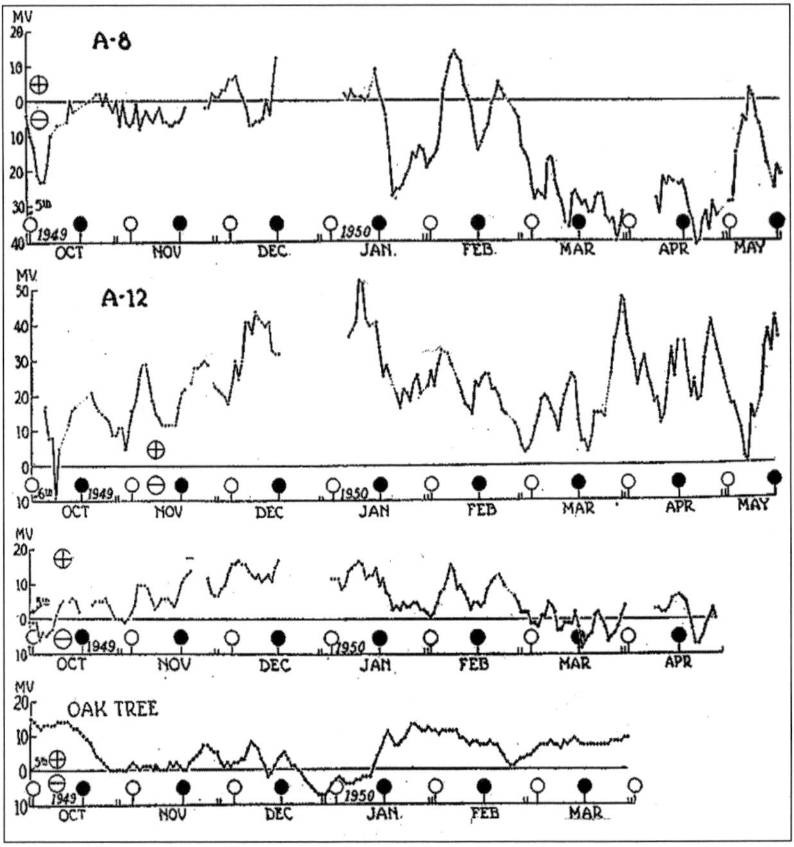

FIG. 18. Algebraic five-day running averages of mean daily field measurements during different moon phases, Yale Medical School, 1949-1950. (Published in L. J. Ravitz: Electrocyclic phenomena and emotional states. *J. Clin. Exp. Psychopath.* 13:69-106, 1952 & Fenómenos electrocíclicos y estados emocionales. *Arch. Med. Internacional y Antib. y Quimiot.* 2: 217-252, 1952.)

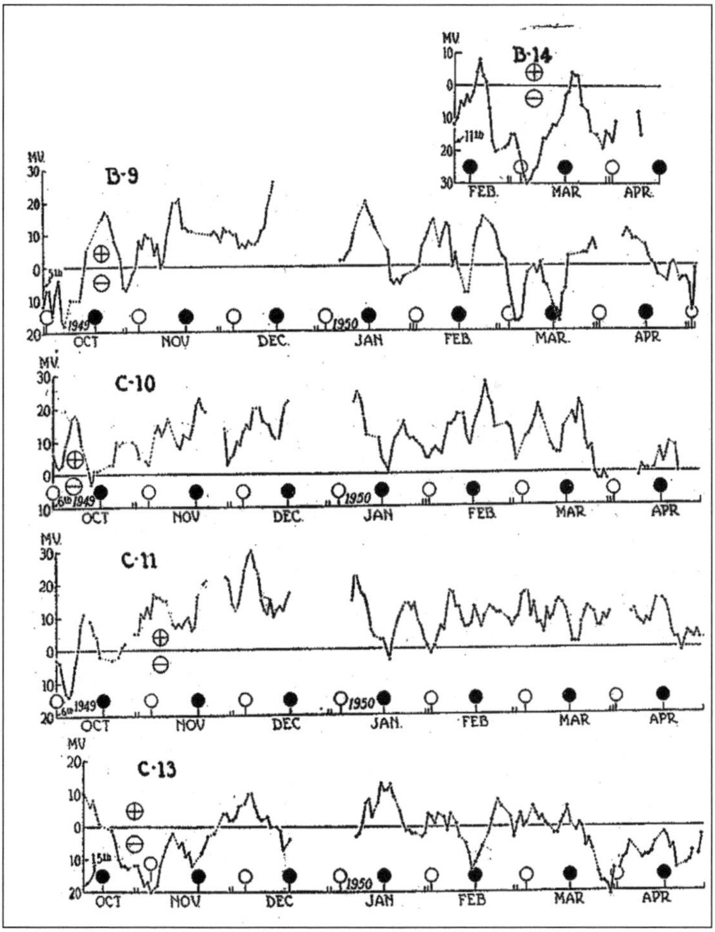

FIG. 19. Algebraic five-day running averages of mean daily field measurements during different moon phases, Yale Medical School, 1949-1950. (Published in L. J. Ravitz: Electrocyclic phenomena and emotional states. *J. Clin. Exp. Psychopath.* 13:69-106, 1952 & Fenómenos electrocíclicos y estados emocionales. *Arch. Med. Internacional y Antib. y Quimiot.* 2: 217-252, 1952.)

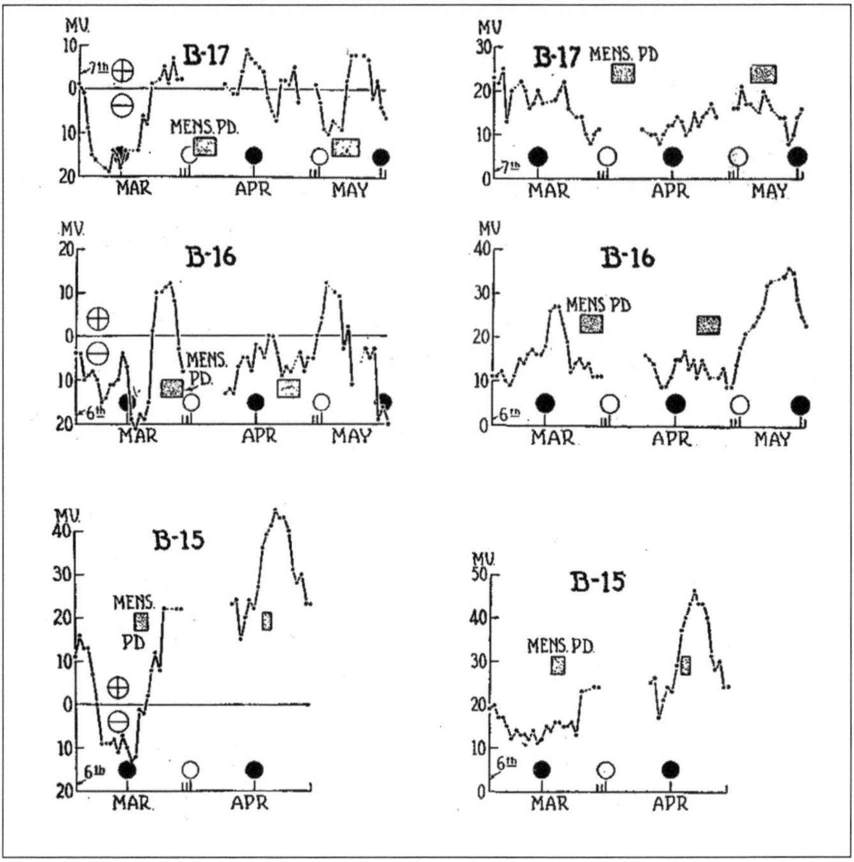

FIG. 20. Algebraic five-day running averages of mean daily field measurements for three females, showing menstrual periods and lunar phases, Yale Medical School, 1950. (Published in L. J. Ravitz: Electrocyclic phenomena and emotional states. *J. Clin. Exp. Psychopath.* 13:69-106, 1952 & Fenómenos electrocíclicos y estados emocionales. *Arch. Med. Internacional y Antib. y Quimiot.* 2: 217-252, 1952.)

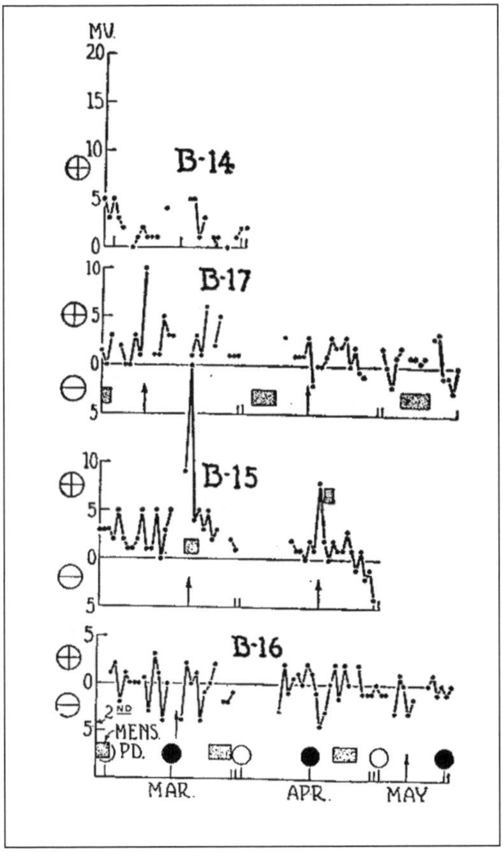

FIG. 21. Algebraic finger potential plots for one male and three females, showing presumed ovulation times (indicated by arrows) and menstrual periods, Yale Medical School, 1950. (Published in L. J. Ravitz: Electrocyclic phenomena and emotional states. *J. Clin. Exp. Psychopath.* 13:69-106, 1952 & Fenómenos electrocíclicos y estados emocionales. *Arch. Med. Internacional y Antib. y Quimiot.* 2: 217-252, 1952.)

Figs. 22-25 show algebraic polar coordinate plots indicating deviations of daily field means from monthly means during different lunar phases for ten subjects and two trees. Fig. 26 shows algebraic five-day running averages of mean daily voltage gradients for six subjects and the oak tree. To illustrate the seasonal cycle more clearly, Fig. 27 shows algebraic eight-month field trends for the six subjects and the oak tree.

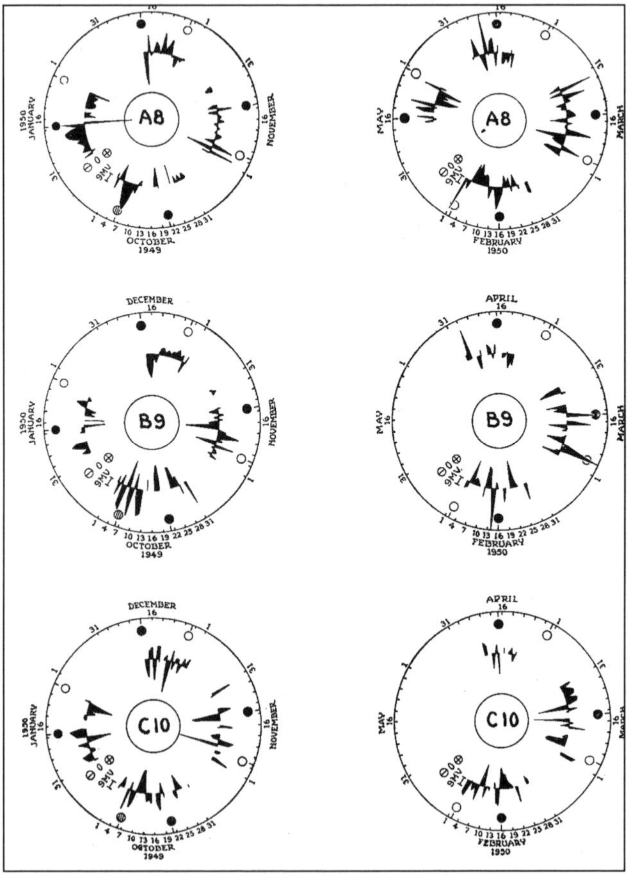

FIG. 22. Algebraic polar coordinate plots showing deviations of daily mean from monthly mean field measurements during different lunar phases for eight months, Yale Medical School, 1949-1950. (Published in L. J. Ravitz: Electrocyclic phenomena and emotional states. *J. Clin. Exp. Psychopath.* 13:69-106, 1952 & Fenómenos electrocíclicos y estados emocionales. *Arch. Med. Internacional y Antib. y Quimiot.* 2: 217-252, 1952.)

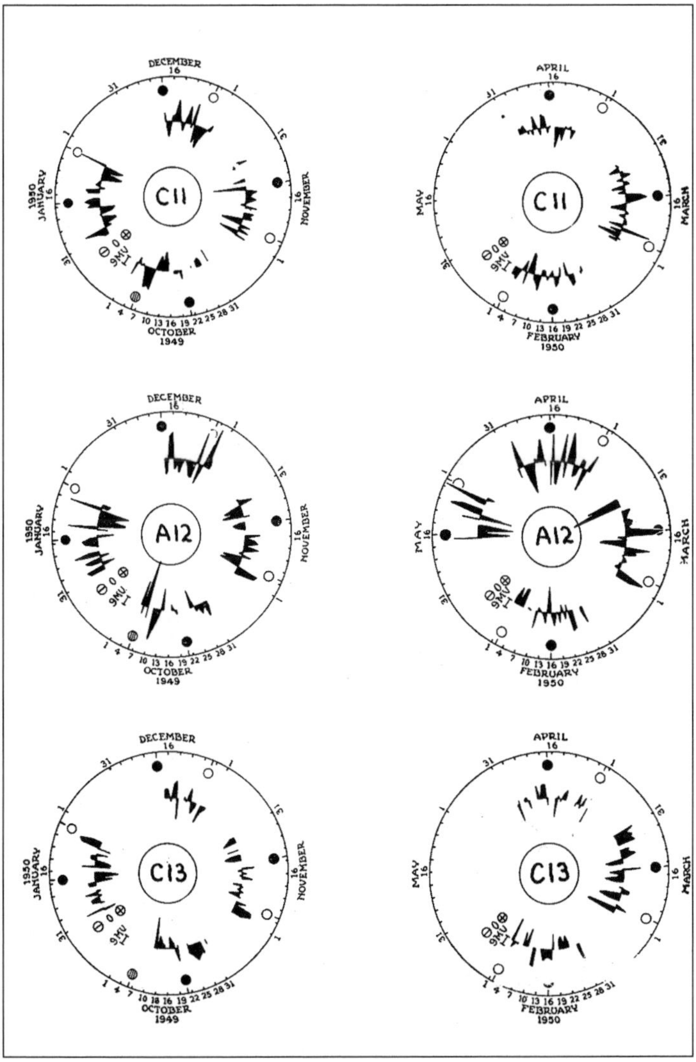

FIG. 23. Algebraic polar coordinate plots showing deviations of daily mean from monthly mean field measurements during different lunar phases for eight months, Yale Medical School, 1949-1950. (Published in L. J. Ravitz: Electrocyclic phenomena and emotional states. *J. Clin. Exp. Psychopath.* 13:69-106, 1952 & Fenómenos electrocíclicos y estados emocionales. *Arch. Med. Internacional y Antib. y Quimiot.* 2: 217-252, 1952.)

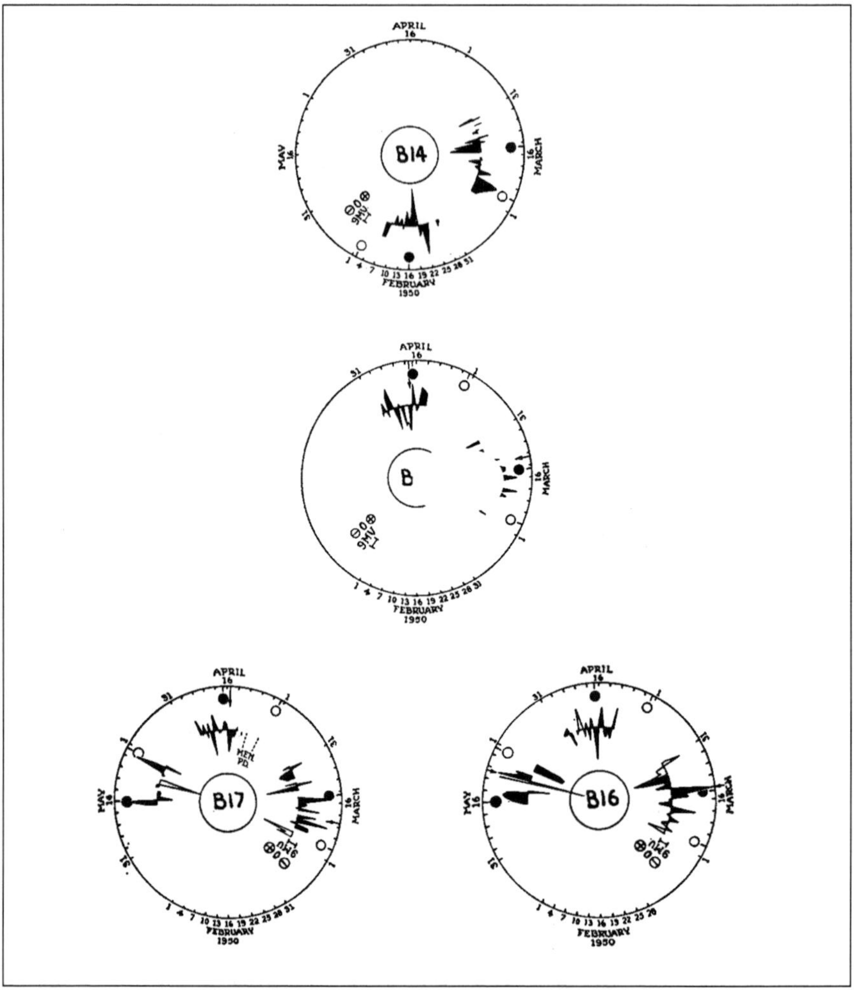

FIG. 24. Algebraic polar coordinate plots showing deviations of daily mean from monthly mean field measurements during different lunar phases for one male and three females, presumed ovulation time (indicated by arrows), and menstrual periods (unshaded portions). Yale Medical School, 1950. (Published in L. J. Ravitz: Electrocyclic phenomena and emotional states. *J. Clin. Exp. Psychopath.* 13:69-106, 1952 & Fenómenos electrocíclicos y estados emocionales. *Arch. Med. Internacional y Antib. y Quimiot.* 2: 217-252, 1952.)

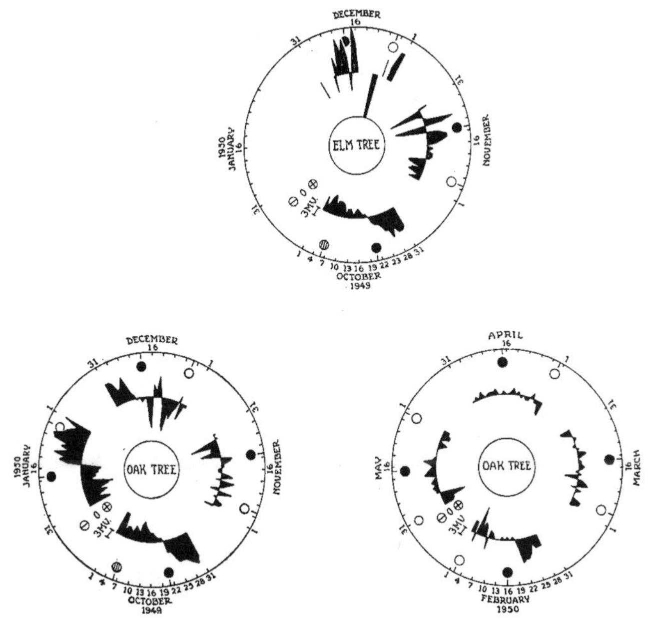

FIG. 25. Algebraic polar coordinate plots showing deviations of daily mean from monthly mean field measurements during different lunar phases for elm and oak trees, New Haven and Lyme, CT, 1949-1950. (Published in L. J. Ravitz: Electrocyclic phenomena and emotional states. *J. Clin. Exp. Psychopath.* 13:69-106, 1952 & Fenómenos electrocíclicos y estados emocionales. *Arch. Med. Internacional y Antib. y Quimiot.* 2: 217-252, 1952.)

In the 1949-1950 group, two subjects became symptomatic during their seasonal field intensifications. A-12 showed a regular cyclic rhythm which was almost uniformly of plus polarity. Apathy, pent-up hostility, aggressiveness, irritability, insecurity and general withdrawal from people usually coincided with average field measurements exceeding *+40* mv. Conversely, enthusiasm, conviviality, general amiability and the subjective feeling of well-being were almost uniformly associated with low plus or minus readings. Like the others, A-12's voltage gradients intensified from October through the first part of January—of significantly higher plus intensifications than the others—and were associated with increasing insecurity, withdrawal, autistic thinking and suspiciousness. This sustained mood was noted by the subject, as was his general improvement during February and March as his voltage gradients detensified. He felt less sensitive to others, enjoyed being with others much more, and was less insecure. Math calculations, which occupied much of his daily work, tended to go more smoothly and he appeared more sociable and less introspective and isolated, occasionally singing and evidencing a dry but keen sense of humor. His best moods generally were correlated with readings below *+12* mv—also rare readings when his head became negative to his chest (his maximal minus reading: *-19.5* mv on May 3, 1950).

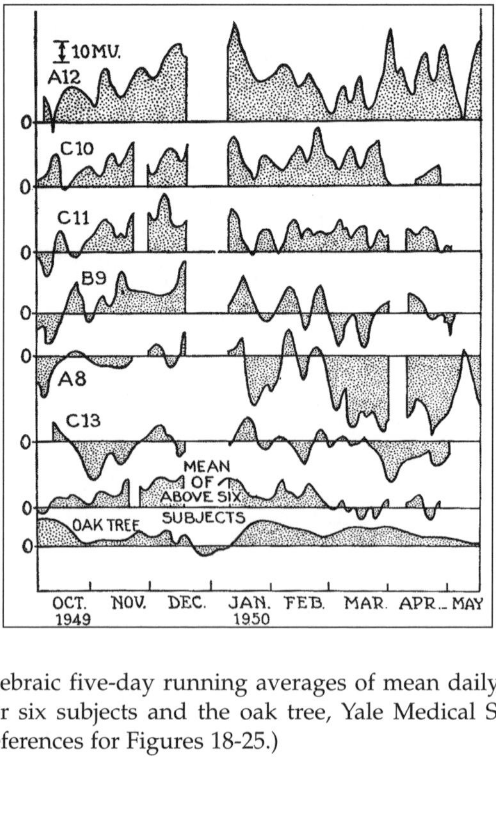

FIG. 26. Algebraic five-day running averages of mean daily field measurements for six subjects and the oak tree, Yale Medical School, 1949-1950. (See references for Figures 18-25.)

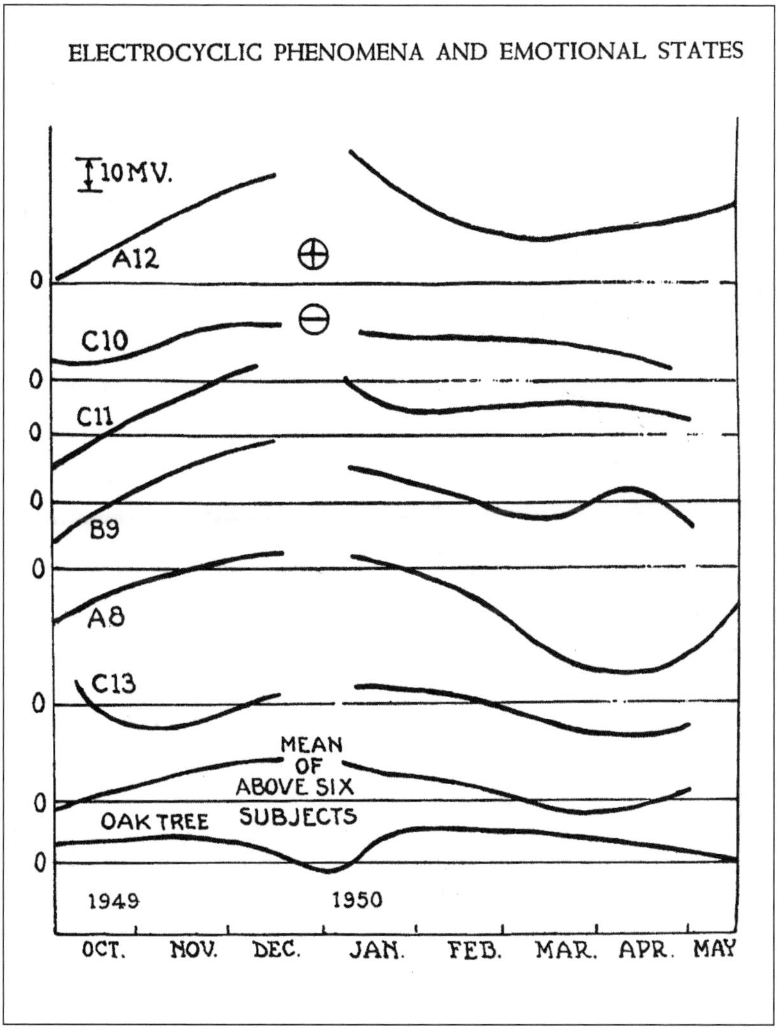

FIG. 27. Algebraic eight-month field trends for six subjects and the oak tree, Yale Medical School, 1949-1950. (See references for Figures 18-25.)

Subject A8 showed considerable polarity fluctuation from October to December 1949. In January, 1950, A8's head tended to become increasingly negative to his chest. At that time he was under pressure studying for mid-year examinations. Toward the end of February until readings were stopped in May, the subject was experiencing conflict with highly emotional interpersonal relationships—correlating with intensifications of minus polarity. During this period, A8 did poorly in his work which he tended to neglect, although his working habits and ability to concentrate improved considerably when satisfactory emotional outlets became available after March despite conflict concerning these situations. Hi-minus readings tended to be associated with gastrointestinal symptoms. Isolated hi-plus or hi-minus measurements were often associated with hyperactivity, tenseness, facetiousness, and emotional lability. As with the other subjects, no correlation was found between body temperature, blood pressure, pulse and field measurements, nor did exercise change the readings significantly in the control subjects.

2

To establish the field as a reliable indicator, it had to be shown that each individual has a field pattern sufficiently stable to allow reasonably accurate, empiric predictions of measurements at specific periods. It was also necessary to show that field measurement variations do reflect the state of the subject whether this can be judged by external criteria or from the subject's feelings which are highly individuated and which may vary from perceiver to perceiver. Despite these limitations and the lack of any psychologic tests of stress, subjective assessments had to be correlated with objective measurements.

Traditional attitudes and a dearth of research funds dictated that these correlations should be governed by conventional statistical procedures. Most of these treat living systems as operating in three-dimensional space and linear-dimensional time. On the other hand, field studies, divested of traditional assumptions, were assessing changes in living matter as it evolved rhythmically and predictably in multidimensional space-time, i.e., in nonlinear, evolving series as regards both intensity, **E** and directional, **H** quantities. Fortunately, through the years, a number of professionally trained volunteer associates became sufficiently interested in these problems to verify many results independently, while subjecting them to relevant statistical approaches.

Despite electrocyclic phenomena which influence field strength and direction, a study by Cuadra of fifty-seven randomly selected patients and controls showed: (1) clear-cut evidence of a high degree of stability for both **E** and **H** measurements over several periods of time, (2) stability is higher when polarity is considered, (3) stability tends to decrease the longer the interval between measurements, and (4) controls showed considerably less stability than hospitalized patients with chronic conditions and perhaps less than the mixed group of hospitalized patients with both semiacute and chronic conditions, Table 6.

This may be due to the fact that undisturbed controls do not tend to maintain high intensities of either polarity. Within circumscribed mean measurement ranges, therefore, small shifts may alter their standing in the group, thereby diluting statistical correlates between their successive measurements.

It should be emphasized that the **E** and **H** field quantities recorded in Table 6 show stability despite electrocyclic phenomena which influence field strength and direction.

TABLE 6
CORRELATIONS BETWEEN CERTAIN ELECTROMAGNETIC FIELD QUANTITIES OF 57 RANDOMLY SELECTED PERSONS OVER SPECIFIC TIME INTERVALS (CUADRA)

Samples	No. of subjects	Periods of comparison	Correlations, monthly means	
			E (intensity)	H (polarity)
Chronic hospitalized patients	15	March verses April	0.82*	0.90*
		April verses May	0.91*	0.91*
		March verses May	0.85*	0.86*
		September verses April	0.21	0.77*
Controls	14	August verses September	-0.04	0.51+
Controls	11	August verses January	-0.13	-0.43
Semiacute and chronic hospitalized patients	17	August verses September	0.21	0.49 ≠

* p <0.001.
\+ p =0.06.
≠ p =0.04.

(Published in L. J. Ravitz: History, measurement, and applicability of periodic changes in the electromagnetic field in health and disease. *An. NY Acad. Sc.* 98: 1144-1201, 1961.)

There are several ways to link voltage gradients with the state of the subject. Aside from the clinical approach which relies largely on observation and even anecdotal material, several formalized rating scales were evolved, sometimes supplemented by psychologic tests. These rating scales made it possible to correlate voltage readings with the subject's assessment of his own feeling states.

Many patients and controls soon learned to predict and correlate their subjective feelings—often so difficult to describe to others—in terms of numeric symbols.

Although subjects had been guessing their field intensities and polarities since 1948, the initial statistical investigation of such potential abilities was made by Cuadra in 1954 on fifteen randomly selected controls. In this particular group, such learned abilities ranged far above chance for most subjects. A few showed phenomenal ability, the correlations between the subjects' predictions and the actual readings being as high as 0.83.

Following this pilot study, special feeling-state scales were further developed by Wilpizeski, Kirby, Stichman and Borghi providing statistical evidence that many subjects can learn to equate their largely ineffable feelings, articulated in imprecise, qualitative symbols, to measurable **E** and **H** field quantities.

Among the experiments with feeling-state scales is one of special significance. Two subjects, 170 and 240, plotted each other's voltage gradients every half-hour over a twenty-four-hour span on March 1 and 2, 1957. Prior to the readings, each person filled out his personal feeling-state inventory in private, which included a guess for both intensity and polarity of the subsequent voltage determinations. Neither subject knew what ratings the other gave himself. Additionally, each subject rated the other subject's behavior. Since each subject in this study was told his past readings, it was thought that much of the correlations between predictions and readings might be accounted for in terms of past knowledge of readings. Concerning the correlations between predictions and feeling-state scales as computed by Wilpizeski and Kirby, many were significant beyond the 0.01 level. At this point, it was considered possible that even higher correlations might be obtained if the subjects were forced to make their predictions purely on the basis of the feeling-state scales without feedback knowledge of past readings. Further, the feeling-state scales of both subjects correlated astonishingly with each other, and definite lags were discovered and timed between relatively precipitous voltage excursions and sharp changes in feeling-state scales. Results of this particular study strongly suggested that both feeling states and readings vary with time.

For shorter term studies in which subjects serve as their own controls before, during and after any given procedure, careful studies were made of changing states before, during and after hypnosis. Such prehypnotic, hypnotic and posthypnotic changes were compared with corresponding alterations in the simultaneously monitored field patterns. Various disquietudes and somatic symptoms were thus recreated, studied electrometrically and compared with those arising spontaneously in nonhypnotic and hypnotic waking states.

Likewise, state changes were studied electrometrically before, during and after the administration of various drugs and placebos and appropriate dosages to achieve the desired experimental effects were compared with field intensity and polarity at given times.

Similarly, the effects of various therapeutic procedures on field measurements were investigated simultaneously. These procedures included carbon dioxide-oxygen inhalation, insulin coma, electroshock, wet packs, tepid tubs and mechanical or psychologic stresses imposed at various points in the cycles of controls and patients. These studies were elaborated further in Chapter 6. Evidence obtained suggested that field changes often precede changes in state by various intervals.

A relationship between somatic and emotive disturbances in hypnotic and nonhypnotic states and field patterns was also established. Somatic symptoms are especially reflected in the polarity, **H** quantity—the hi-minus field form tending to be characteristic of preadolescent and aging adult groups.

Infectious diseases and other periodic clinical symptoms, such as peptic ulcers and allergies, tend to coincide with seasonal field shifts. The onset of symptoms often correlates with diurnal variations. Such findings are detailed in Chapter 13.

3

Correspondences between celestial motions and various biologic rhythms have been noted since the days of antiquity. For example, certain writings attributed to Hippocrates show so strong a faith in cosmic influence on distempers that "the first citizen of Cos" specifically recommended that physicians ignorant of astronomy be viewed with a jaundiced eye. So also Galen, who especially emphasized the moon. Lunations were said to correspond to the patient's sufferings. These critical days, later called crises, comprised the seventh, fourteenth and twenty-first of the disease—intervals between lunar syzygies and quadratures. Yet the kernel of truth residing in such observations became so camouflaged by astrologic mummery that they dropped out of fashion. In fact, until recently, anyone brave enough to aver periodic phenomena ran the risk of being accused of quackery.

In two cautious references to periodicities, Darwin first suggested that vertebrates and insects are subjected to "that mysterious law, which causes certain normal processes, such as gestation, as well as the maturation and duration of various diseases, to follow lunar periods." He then tentatively postulated, in a footnote, that gestation, duration of fevers, hatching of eggs, etc. might represent tidal vestiges from phylogenetically ancient prototypes allied to existing ascidians.

The mid-19th-century recrudescence of interest in periodicities, however, was more overtly concerned with human sexual rhythms. Ellis summarized evidence for such rhythmicity, noting the emphasis of Laycock and Smith on fractions and multiples of seven days as well as equinoctial perturbations of all sorts.

Concerning human beings, two additional empiric investigations merit notice. Following the isolation of 27.32156-day tropical lunar tides in the electric potential gradients of the atmosphere by Ekholm and Arrhenius, the latter was able to show that menstruation, nativity, seizures and other biologic processes are partially dependent on rhythmic meteorologic factors which assert their presence and pull in conjunction with other forces. Petersen demonstrated various extraterrestrial correlations supported by results of his own experiments.

Moreover, despite the existence of definite seasonal and annual periods for many infectious diseases, these are now generally thought to be under human control, evidence for epidemic ebb and flow being disregarded. Thus, aside from meteorologic investigations, current interest in cyclic phenomena remains largely confined to rhythmic behavior in less differentiated creatures, e.g., homing, migratory, food-gathering and reproductive activities. About 250 years after the Royal Society had considered verification of ancient Greek maxims regarding lunar periodicities in shellfish (1667), the question was finally answered by Fox, who discovered a rhythmicity in the Red Sea variety, but none in their Mediterranean cousins. Similar investigation found lunar rhythms in numerous littoral organisms. Since 1954, Brown and associates have published results of experiments demonstrating cycles of varying frequencies in several invertebrates, amphibians, vegetables, plants and rats. Contrary to general opinion, their studies have also indicated that diurnal cycles in aquatic organisms are uninfluenced by variations in temperature and illumination. As an alternative explanation for biologic rhythms, Brown suggested periodicities in cosmic-ray emission.

4

Despite such findings, any traditional Baconian search for unifying principles applicable to both the animate and inanimate domains has inherent limitations. Man's dim sensory equipment requires amplification to gain even a beginning understanding of all the entities and relationships swirling about and within him. It follows that carefully formulated abstract hunches, or constructs, become necessary to designate unsensed theoretic factors with sufficient precision to permit empiric verification.

In the modern era, the first known scientific attempt to subsume living systems under natural laws was made by Newton. In his "Second Paper on Light & Colours," presented to the Royal Society on December 9, 1675, but not published until 1757, an electromagnetic-like "subtle...vibrating...electric and elastic medium" was introduced—the inorganic basis of life. This irreducible theoretic component governed various properties of living and nonliving substances alike. Moreover, by exciting such disparate phenomena as repulsion, attraction, sensation and motion, Newton's common denominator anticipated the electromagnetic field of Faraday and Maxwell. Portions of the theory were elaborated as an expanding series of "Queries" published in successive editions of his book *Opticks*. By this means, propositions which Newton considered overspeculative and experimentally incomplete were framed as questions.

Next, in 1704, Richard Mead, the noted eighteenth-century British physician and second holder of the Goldheaded Cane, made an attempt to place living systems under the laws of Newtonian mechanics. Initially, he elaborated a theory of atmospheric tides, supposedly caused by gravitational effects of sun and moon, which could exist independently of barometric changes. By causing periodic shifts in atmospheric gravity, elasticity and pressure, these tides acted as an "external assistance," to the "inward causes" or "nervous fluid" prevailing in animal bodies. In 1704, Mead published his early propositions in *De Imperio Solis ac Lunae in Corpora Humana, et Morbis inde Oriundis,* translated in subsequent widely disseminated editions. By 1747, stimulated by Newton's "Queries" and the experiments of Gray and DuFay, Mead had equated the "nervous fluid" with electricity.

Both Nollet and Freke published related theories and experiments in 1747 and 1752, respectively. Next to toss his hat into the ring was Mesmer, who plagiarized Mead's idea of atmospheric tides (Pattie). To the tidal theory, he appended the notion of animal tides and added several concepts, some of which bear striking similarity to Newton's irreducible "vibrating...electric and elastic spirit." At first, Mesmer naively called the force "animal gravitation," but in 1775 he changed its name to "animal magnetism." The medium which filled celestial space was believed capable of acting on the nervous system of animate forms directly, depending on individuated tidal resonances in human bodies. Such harmonics were supposedly attuned to specific astronomic configurations.

Other exponents of electricity in living things included Mauduit and Bertholon, the latter publishing in 1783 the first experiments providing evidence for the influence of atmospheric electricity on vegetation. Despite such interest, after Galvani's famed dispute with Fabroni and Volta in 1792, electricity jumped into the laps of the physicists. There, with such notable exceptions as the studies of Faraday and DuBois-Reymond, it remained until the late nineteenth century.

Though cycles in terrestrial magnetism had long been noted and various hypotheses advanced, the exogenous tidal component of Mead's theory was first reformulated most accurately by Stewart, who in 1883 posited electric conductivity of the earth's upper atmosphere. In more recent years, lunar tides in the ionosphere showing undulations of a mile or more have been discovered by bouncing radio signals from the ionosphere. These rhythms produce concomitant cycles of cosmic-ray meson showers bombarding the earth. Periodicities of other frequencies have been demonstrated not only in the ionosphere, but also in the sun's electromagnetic field. Moreover, the apparent relationship of solar activity to certain planetary configurations enabled Nelson to develop a system for forecasting the strength of shortwave radio transmission for RCA Communications, which has attained an accuracy of 88 percent.

5

The second portion of Mead's propositions was most systematically brought up-to-date by Burr and Northrop. In brief, they felt that as classic particle physics required supplementation with field constructs in the inorganic realm, the same should hold true in the biologic domain. In other words, there must be some force behind the constituents of living things capable of organizing, directing and holding them together during the complex chemical interchanges accompanying biologic processes. A steadily increasing stream of evidence was accumulating which attested to the fundamental nature of basic electric properties in protoplasmic systems. Yet the results could be considered reproducible only in a general sense since the measuring devices, with few exceptions, drained the requisite power from the creature being measured. When in 1935, the Burr-Lane-Nims micro- and millivoltmeters were developed, there were at last instruments capable of measuring minute, slowly changing voltage differences without appreciably affecting the organism under study. Put into operation, these measuring devices detected what theory proposed: in their theoretic component, living things are indeed electric systems exhibiting reproducible electromagnetic field properties continuously in multidimensional space-time.

Details of numerous experiments which demonstrate the ubiquitous and fundamental nature of such field properties have since been published. Suffice it to say, by 1943 Mead's construct of tidal atmospheric influence, Mesmer's additional designation of animal tides and Bertholon's experiments on the electric attributes of vegetation were finally approaching scientific confirmation by continuous recordings of voltage differences between two electrodes embedded in the cambia of elm, oak and maple trees. These potential gradients showed predictable variations especially in the form of diurnal, monthly, seasonal, semiannual and annual cycles.

6

Finally, in 1948 the first of two singular discoveries based on the Burr-Northrop *Theory* gave further scientific confirmation to the influence of electromagnetic phenomena on living systems.

Previous mention has been made of the fact that on April 24, 1948, the depth of hypnosis, which heretofore had eluded objective measurement, was electrometrically recorded for the first time and compared with field shifts during other state changes. As hypnotic states involve electromagnetic flux and reflux, Maxwell's equations can be blamed for inadvertently resurrecting that much maligned wraith, Mesmer's "animal magnetism," now more suitably clad in the garb of modern field physics.

Then in 1949, an extraordinary discovery in human biology was made. Despite the multitude of highly individuated variables encountered, long-range studies on human subjects revealed unequivocal electrocyclic phenomena identical to those of trees, including fortnightly periods. Over 75,000 field determinations on over 500 human subjects at Yale, Duke and the University of Pennsylvania Schools of Medicine; the Roanoke and Downey Veterans Administration Hospitals; Eastern State Hospital (Williamsburg, Virginia) and in private practice indicate that these cyclic variations provide objective profiles of variations in feeling and behavior states which often transcend observable criteria. Statistical evaluation of such measurements has shown the highest known correlates between any physiologic measuring technique and estimates of severity of symptoms. Ranging from *states of excitation* to *states of exhaustion,* electrocyclic phenomena also open the door both to long- and short-range predictions.

Thus it happened that experiments at long last were able to cast light on Newton's "most subtle...electric and elastic spirit which pervades and lies hid in all gross bodies...;" and reinforce his supposition that "by the force and action of which spirit...all sensation is excited, and the members of animal bodies move...namely, by the vibrations of this spirit..."

Electrometric readings finally furnished scientific explanations for certain aspects of age-old beliefs ascribing various changes in statefunction to the lunar cycle with, however, several new twists, viz., the dependency of such changes on individual responsiveness and individual reaction times to individually timed rhythmic variations, whose intensities, elasticities and directions are amplified, condensed, accelerated, decelerated and reversed in accord with periods of other frequencies. Beyond all this frenetic energy flow and ebb, the moon remains silently aloof being itself propelled into space-time along invisible tracks of its own course by the same forces operating upon and within living matter.

7

With human subjects, maximal voltage variations may precede

and/or follow the twenty-four-hour lunar syzygy day. Sometimes voltage peaks occur one to four days before the syzygy and/or one to four days after.

These lunar field intensifications vary with the season. At new moon phase in winter in the northern hemisphere, field intensifications tend to accelerate in a plus direction, then swing minus in late spring and early summer. During the winter full moon phase field intensifications tend to accelerate in a minus direction, relative to those at new moon.

Such changes vary with the individual. Some tend to spike plus both at new and full moon periods during winter, though at new moon in winter plus increases are greater than at full moon. To make things more complicated, EMF spikes during lunations are affected by annual, seasonal, weekly and diurnal rhythms. The greatest plus spikes usually occur in December and January, especially during a January new moon phase, while the greatest minus spikes tend to occur in June and July. During March, Wilpizeski has found the lunar field cycle is likely to disappear.

Fig. 28, a statistical analysis by Wilpizeski, shows parallel seasonal trendlines for three parakeets, seventy-five human subjects (thirty of whom were controls and forty-five chronic schizophrenic patients at Downey Veterans Administration Hospital, North Chicago, Illinois) and an aged elm tree at Lyme, Connecticut, 1000 miles east. Simultaneous curves are plotted as five-day moving **E** and **H** field means for these human, avian and tree subjects. Spring and summer lunar syzygies for 1954 are also indicated.

The trendlines of these samples from animal and plant kingdoms parallel each other even though different measuring techniques were used for each sample. Monthly sinusoidal curves characterized by opposite polar excursions are demonstrated, and characteristic periodic movements (described as percentage deviations from the trendlines) show increased stability in less differentiated living systems.

8

Relativity seems the rule for these electric tides of life. Many factors, including age and sex, influence them simultaneously. For example, in the northern hemisphere those who experience seizures or migraine at hi-plus EMF will tend to have exacerbations in the winter months. In summer, they may be free of seizures during the day and early evening. Some, however, particularly at syzygies, suddenly spike very high field intensities late at night or in the very early morning hours, and these spikes are accompanied by nocturnal convulsions and/or migraine.

In January, one person may develop seizures forty-eight hours after new moon at 8:00 a.m. and be free of seizures at June and July syzygy periods. Another may have only nocturnal seizures limited to early summer full moon phases. A third may have seizures limited to the January new moon phase.

Seizure incidence varies with the individual and at times can be triggered by alcohol and other drugs, tobacco, insufficient sleep or stress.

Despite these random influences, however, cycles are clearly discernible. Moreover, with hi-minus EMF, individuals may experience various perturbations in early summer which are neither seizures nor migraine and which are sometimes combined with somatic symptoms. Another group tends to show disquietudes in September—the hurricane season in northern latitudes—which is accompanied by marked variable EMF intensifications. These, of course, are influenced by age and sex.

For example, on December 23, 1972, GSI, age thirty-one, noted sixteen sequential seizures between June 1, 1968, and November

5,1972, only two of which occurred on the exact syzygy day (new moon). Table 7 denotes lunation as well as pre-/post-syzygy days compared with his maximal/minimal seizure frequencies. Table 8 shows sequential pre-/post-syzygy days compared with seizure frequencies. In this instance, most of the seizures occurred at two days before new moon (n_{-2}), one day before new moon (n_{-1}), at new moon (n_o), four days after new moon (n_{+4}), two days after full moon (f_{+2}) and three days after full moon (f_{+3})—most seizure frequencies occurring within four days before and/or after the precise syzygy day. During these intervals, seizures occurred only in the five months shown in Table 9—75% developing in June and November.

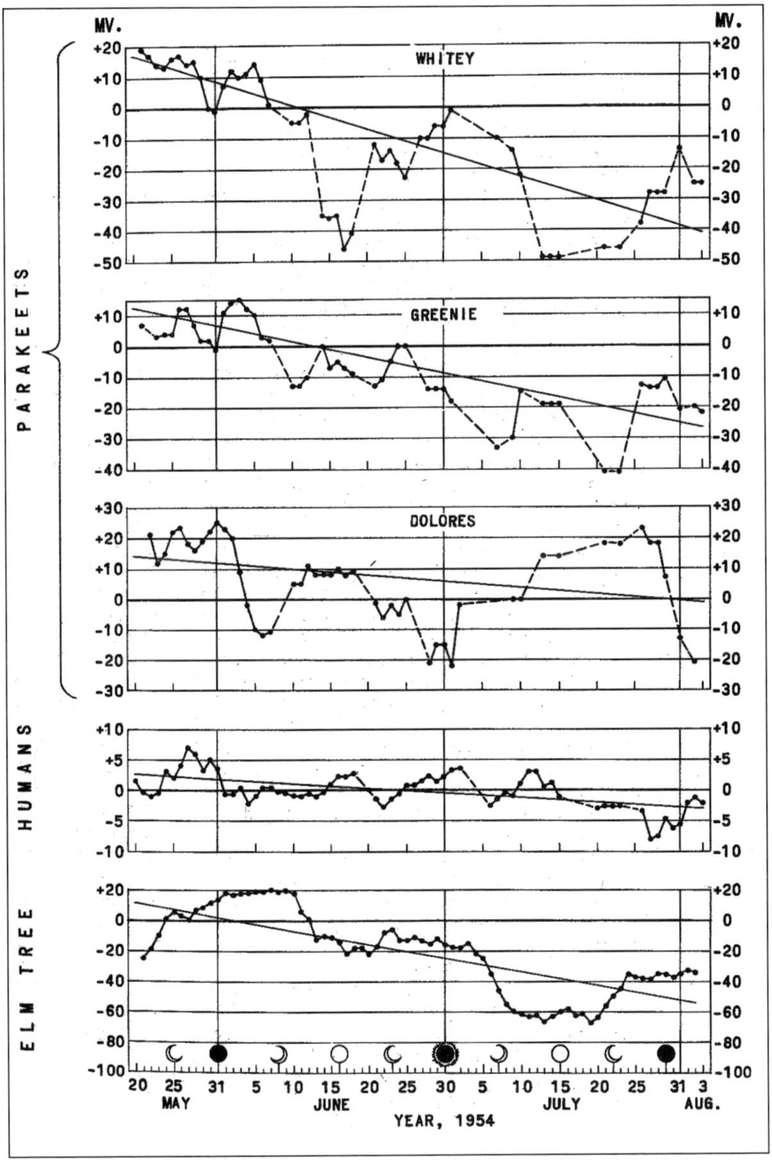

FIG 28. Parallel seasonal statistical trendlines for three parakeets and seventy-five human subjects (thirty controls and forty-five chronic schizophrenic patients), Downey VA Hospital, N. Chicago, IL, v. a Lyme, CT and elm free 1000 miles away, simultaneously plotted as five-day moving **E** and **H** field means, also showing lunar phases, late spring and summer 1954. Calculations and graphing by Chester R. Wilpizeski, Ph. D. (Published in L. J. Ravitz: Systematic experimental extension of multidimensional relativity field physics to biology and medicine. *et al.* 4, no. 1:28-49, 1976.)

TABLE 7
LUNATION±4 DAYS VERSUS 16 MAXIMAL-MINIMAL SEIZURE FREQUENCIES, SUBJECT GSI, JUNE 1, 1968-N0VEMBER 5, 1972

Syzygy period	Seizure frequency
f_{+2}	3
f_{+3}	2
n_{-2}	.2
n_{-1}	2
n_{0}	2
n_{+4}	.2
n_{-3}	.1
n_{+1}	..1
n_{+2}	...1
Total seizures	16

TABLE 8
SEQUENTIAL PRE- AND POST-LUNAR SYZYGY DAYS VERSUS SEIZURE FREQUENCIES

New-moon phase	Seizure frequency	Full-moon phase	Seizure frequency
(n_{-4})	0	(f_{-4})	0
$^*n_{-3}$	1	(f_{-3})	0
$^*n_{-2}$	2	(f_{-2})	0
$^*n_{-1}$	2	(f_{1})	0
$^*n_{0}$	2	(f_{0})	0
$^*n_{+1}$	1	(f_{+1})	0
$^*n_{+2}$	1	(f_{+2})	3
(n_{+3})	0	(f_{+3})	2
$^*n_{+4}$	2	(f_{+4})	0

f= full moon
n = new moon
*n = new moon seizure periods
Parentheses indicate seizure-free days

TABLE 9
MONTHS VERSUS 16 SEIZURE FREQUENCIES, TABLES 7 & 8

Months	Seizure frequency		%
*June	8		50.00
*November	4		25.00
February	2	12.50	
January	1	6.25	25.00
March	1	6.25	
Total seizures	16		100.00

*Asterisks denote months in which maximal seizures occurred.

In short, state perturbations are inevitably reflected in fluxes and refluxes of electromagnetic or electrodynamic fields which vary with measurable rhythms. In other words, they can be equated with measurable energy.

9

Chronic inert schizophrenic patient 103 described in Chapter 9 is an example of further correlations between electrocyclic phenomena and periodic statefunction changes in humans. With extremely high variable field intensifications, mute, torpid, trashcollecting Subject 103 showed marked curiousity about his torpid intervals, if indeed during these he registered anything. During such brief periods of high variable field intensifications, he even learned to predict his own readings.

As voltages began to detensify, however, he entered a transitional state: his face became less mobile, his speech quieter, his motor behavior slower, and he lost the ability to concentrate. On May 20, 1954, a 400% intensity drop of *+64* to *+16* mv was recorded within one minute, and seconds later he was inert.

Fig. 14A shows resistive behavior changes from his usual mute, torpid, trash-collecting state illustrated in Fig. 14B. Though he remained with a frozen stare, between 9:04 a.m. and 1:50 p.m., his voltage gradients intensified moderately from *+27* mv to *+39* mv. This occurred one day before the full moon on June 15, 1954

Fig. 14C on June 25, 3:20 p.m., shows a steady mean EMF of *+43* mv before exercising. Slightly animated, he responded to questions, was pleasant and cooperative without his frozen stare and studied his previous EMF readings. At 3:23 p.m. after exercising, his voltage gradients intensified to a steady *+60* mv and he showed increased animation, Fig. 14D.

By July 1, one day following new moon and solar eclipse, (103)'s usual mute, torpid state had changed dramatically. He was suddenly alert, friendly, beaming and articulate. Fig. 14E prior to exercising at 1:30 p.m., shows his field measurement *-40* mv of mixed polarity, predominantly minus, with moderate variability which was associated with mild animation. Fig. 14F after exercising at 1:43 p.m., shows an EMF intensification in the plus direction. There was marked variability (46 mv range: *+68* to *+114* mv) and during this time, 103 was very animated.

Two days prior to full moon on July 13, his voltage gradients before exercising (not pictured) were *+85* mv, with variations from *+76* mv to *+94* mv. Subject was animated, friendly and reviewed his own records. His dramatic improvement was similar to that of July 1.

Figs. 14G and 14H show that, at 1:42 p.m. after exercising, his EMF intensified 41 mv to *+126* mv and he was exuberant. By next morning, however, his EMF had dropped to a steady *+38* mv, and he had returned to his usual mute, torpid, trash-collecting state.

As we have seen, at times 103's voltage gradients could be plus intensified to varying degrees with exercise. Yet if his EMF intensities were decreasing, repeated exercise had diminishing effects until finally, if the intensity fell below a certain level, the patient failed to respond. He was housed in a control ward with forty-four other chronic schizophrenic patients—all male, about the same age and obviously psychotic for the same time intervals.

Curiously, the average field intensification during ovulation, which can spike to over 100 mv, Fig. 4, corresponds to the same mean levels found in disturbed schizophrenic patients, chronic inert schizophrenics at brief periods of rare optimal functioning, Tables 2 and 3, and in trees just before and during the hurricane of September 14, 1944.

Chapter Thirteen

THE MIRROR OF LIFE

1

We may look on the human electromagnetic field as a special kind of mirror which can both cause and reflect most, if not all, conditions of the human organism, physical and emotional. Unlike ordinary mirrors it can reflect and reveal conditions invisible to the eye and beyond the scope of conventional diagnostic procedures and can also give advance warning of changing physical and emotional states. In this chapter, we will consider some random examples of what this "mirror" can show us.

Adult human subjects, as well as other forms of life, run down electrically as they get older and, as we would expect, this shows up in field measurements. With head-chest electrode placements, these measurements tend to show a minus polarity reversal. By taking regular measurements over a period on any given individual, it would be possible to assess the rate at which his battery is running down. But as most elderly people are painfully conscious of failing energies, it is unlikely that they would want depressing electrometric confirmation!

At the other end of life, incidentally, infants and preadolescent children also tend to show predominant minus polarity.

Disorders associated with aging, such as malignancies or arthritis, show EMF correlates in the minus polarity range.

Typical Caucasian men during adolescence and early adulthood usually exhibit moderately hi-plus intensities of considerable variability, and the unstable energies of late adolescent males parallel their statistically demonstrated tendency to automobile accidents. Young adult males stuck in the hi-minus range seem liable to somatic disorders.

Pilot studies suggest that Orientals may tend to show more minus readings than Caucasians at the same age, relatively pure Negroes tending to show greater field intensifications of plus polarity.

On the other hand, Caucasian women dip minus much earlier than men. By the third decade in most women measured, the readings tend to be stabilized within the minus to low-plus range. Men in their thirties show marked individual variations regarding polarity signs. Beyond age fifty, however, sustained plus polarity has been found relatively infrequently, with individual exceptions. Likewise, voltage variability is characteristically reduced with aging, although again individual exceptions occur. Contracted field variability after age sixty-five has been noted in patients showing signs of deterioration. In those whose typical readings are restricted to the minus range, any significant excursions in the plus direction are usually associated with irritability and other feelings of disquietude.

On inspection, the most common symptom linked with relatively sustained voltage levels is fatigue. Numerous somatic complaints crop up at such sustained values in the hi-minus range.

On the other hand, the "energy of youth," its elasticity, lability and its many violent manifestations in adolescent and early adult males particularly, now can be considered in terms of primary factors which in those so predisposed, appear to trigger the onset of various disorders. Among these are schizophrenia, migraine and seizure states. By the same token, the fact that certain disorders in some individuals are "outgrown," or disappear with aging, can for the first time be viewed relative to continuously changing, irreducible electromagnetic field properties.

Aside from exemplifying the nonspecific property of field measurements, these studies highlight the inherent impotence of bifurcated "psychosomatic" constructs. Emotional and physical factors appear indistinguishably and inexorably welded to individuated variable baseline states of given organisms in space-time, defined relative to certain electromagnetic field parameters. Moreover, through this new definition of state, not only is light shed on the known periodicities of certain clinical conditions including many of the common infectious diseases, but also on the profound and protracted psychiatric, surgical and medical problems often encountered in geriatric patients.

2

As previously noted, somatic symptoms show correlates especially with changes in the polarity or **H** quantity of field variables, which likewise undergo characteristic alterations with aging. The following outline indicates certain linkages, some of which are exemplified in summary form:

(a) Changes in statefunction principally involving the **H** quantity, preceded by or associated with field shifts in the minus direction:

i.Common infectious diseases including upper respiratory infections (e.g., comments on subject (A)71, Fig. 15)

ii.Peptic ulcers and other benign gastrointestinal disorders (e.g., comments on subject 157)

iii.Allergies (e.g., asthma and hay fever, the latter exempli fied in Table 10 which shows the development of hay fever symptoms after full moon in patient (204), a psychotic woman undergoing insulin-coma treatments)

TABLE 10
FIELD CORRELATIONS OF STATE CHANGES DURING AND FOLLOWING SUCCESSIVE LUNAR SYZYGIES IN PATIENT 204, A 24-YEAR-OLD WOMAN RECIEVING INSULIN-COMA TREATMENTS FOR AN ACUTELY DISTURBED SCHIZOPHRENIC EPISODE

University of Pennsylvania Medical School, Philadelphia, PA, 1955.

Date 1955	Means E	Means H	Lunation	Summaries of nursing notes: Behavior	Summaries of nursing notes: Somatic symptoms and menses
8/17	7	-7	n_0 *	Fairly cooperative; somewhat lethargic	None
8/18	-	-	n_{+1}	To disturbed ward; behavior precluded measurements	None
8/19	47	+47	n_{+2}	Sarcastic; rude; continually demanding	Day 1, menses
8/20	-	-	n_{+3}	Same (technician absent)	Day 2, menses
8/21	29	+29	n_{+4}	Crying; angry: tried to choke nurse; to disturbed ward again	Day 3, menses
8/22	17	+17	n_{+5}	Less demanding, seeking comfort and companionship	None
8/23	28	+28	n_{+6}	Sarcastic; loud and raucous; slovenly	None
9/1	0	0	f_{-1} †	Slept a great deal (unusual) today; friendly	None
9/2	18	-18	f_0	Thought she was dying after insulin; premature wakening requesting anti-histamine for hay fever	Severe hay fever symptoms; many somatic complaints
9/3	6	-6	f_{+1}	Appetite improved; likewise sleep and behavior	Hay fever improved
9/4	15	-15	f_{+2}	Usually loud and rowdy, but related well with others	Hay fever symptoms increased. On anti-histamines
9/5	21	-21	f_{+3}	Loud; obstreperous; pacing, belligerent toward nurses; friendly toward patients	Hay fever symptoms, especially previous night
9/6	41	+41	f_{+4}	Great variability; not quiet for more than five minutes all day; enraged other patients; *no insulin reaction;* depersonalized later; irratable; excitable; raging	None
9/7	0	0	f_{+5}	Cooperative and pleasant to contentious; much more quiet and cooperative	None

* n = new moon
† *f* = full moon

(Published in L. J. Ravitz: History, measurement, and applicability of periodic changes in the electromagnetic field in health and disease. *An. NY Acad Sc.* 98: 1144-1201, 1962.)

iv. Carbuncles and furuncles

v. Arthritis

vi. Wounds (see Burr et al.)

vii. Nonspecific "psychosomatic" complaints (e.g., Subject 157). The case of subject DFD also illustrates the presence of such symptoms at hi-minus field configurations and their amelioration via hypnosis, accompanied by a polar reversal. This subject felt torpid, logy, generally uncomfortable and warm, likewise noting aches and pains on the evening of January 21, 1959, at a special seminar. At 9:03 p.m., a trance was induced after the subjects prehypnotic readings had been taken (*-40* mv). Following trance termination at 10:30 p.m., from which state he emerged smiling, his field patterns stabilized at zero. Although nonspecific allusions to symptoms had been made, he was now facetious and symptom-free but sleepy, a feeling he desired to have since it was time for him to return home and go to bed. DFD also had a history of peptic ulcers. The possibility that his late evening, diurnal electrocyclic shifts toward positivity were potentiated through hypnosis is suggested by effects of a subsequent trance state which was induced on the evening of January 26 at an earlier hour, 8:26 p.m. (*-37* mv), at which time he had a head cold and noted similar complaints on his rating scales. Following stabilization of his field patterns after trance termination at 9:30 p.m. (*-26* mv), he indicated less aches and pains and felt more talkative, but by no means was symptom-free.

viii. Peripheral nerve injuries (see Grenell and Burr)

ix. Cellular growth, i.e., the growing portion (see Mathews, Ingvar, Lund, Burr et al.)

x. Infancy

xi. Aging in adults

xii. Malignancies. In November 1956, Subject 246.3, a sixty-five-year-old woman who suffered from cataracts and beginning arthritis, was vacationing. Her field patterns showed unusually high magnitudes of uniformly minus polarity, intensifications of which correlated with agitation, loquacity or general excitability and irritability. When sustained, such hi-minus readings accompanied profound fatigue. During that period, subject 246.3's voltage gradients averaged *-49* mv, as contrasted with those of her symptom-free sixty-eight-year-old husband, whose mean over the same span of time was *+1* mv.

On June 14, 1961, she was scheduled to undergo removal of most of the sigmoid for two Grade-2, Stage2 adeno carcinomas at each end. Voltage means on June 13 were *-46* mv having shown slight intensity decrements from - *48* to *-43* mv the night before surgery. Following surgery, with symptoms of nausea, she showed a relatively steady pattern, ranging from *-50* to *-53* mv. It was necessary for a nurse to fill out her subjective rating scales. The next day she felt just as ill (*-68* mv). By late afternon, she felt sufficiently improved to request another field measurement (*-58* mv). That evening she developed a spurt of energy and felt less pain, which correlated with relatively precipitous excursions in the minus direction (*-73* mv). With a generally sustained level in the waking state at the same values (*-73* mv), subject 246.3 felt very depressed the following day. This was com pounded by considerable irratability that afternoon (*-80* mv). The following day, on June 17 she became very irritated with the nurse (*-87* mv). Later in the afternoon, she was found crying (*-85* mv). The mean of these pre- and post operative reading was *-65* mv. Her husband's mean over the same period was *+3* mv; that of a thirty-six-year-old son, *+4* mv and that of a nurse some ten years her junior, *-16* mv. On June 15 and 16, it was possible to compare her means with those of two cousins who were measured at about the same time.

The relatively symptom-free cousin (age seventy-six) averaged *-23* mv. The other cousin (age eighty) who suffered from chronic "psychosomatic" symptoms showed a *-45* mv mean.

When next seen, from September 3 to 7, 1961, subject 246.3 had made an uneventful recovery. Her voltage means now averaged *-18* mv; those of her husband, *0* mv and those of her son, *-19* mv.

The voltage findings in subject 246.3 corroborate those of Langman and Burr, indicating that with the development of malignancy, and perhaps even before, certain aspects of the field pattern of the entire organism show nonspecific intensifications in the minus direction.

xiii. Oppressive fatigue

xiv. Oppressive sleepiness

(b) Changes in statefunction principally involving the **E** quantity, preceded by or associated with field shifts to high intensification, the polar direction of which appears to be conditioned by individuated electrocyclic variables:

i. Moderately severe to severe headaches other than migraine

ii. Seizure states. In January 1952, subject 70, an eighteen-year-old student, decided to join his mother and sister in undergoing field monitoring of his changing statefunction on a daily basis. The sister was an epileptic suffering from mixed seizure states; the mother, who had a similar condition in her earlier years, "outgrew" them. So far as is known, Subject 70 was seizure-free. His field profile showed moderately high intensities of plus polarity, characteristic for youths of his age at this time of the year. During the week beginning on January 30, his daily mean field measurements had dropped to *-11* mv. Successive daily means through January 26 were respectively: *+1,+4, +9, -2, +1*, and *-1* mv. On Sunday morning, January 27, his readings showed an acceleration, leveling off at *+58* mv, 59 mv higher than his previous daily mean. Two minutes after measurements, Subject 70 suffered a seizure. He was unconscious for sixty seconds, then groggy for the next five minutes. There were no tonic or clonic phases. In the course of sixty mean daily field determinations, he failed to show any daily variability exceeding that between January 26 and 27. On January 28, his voltage mean had dropped to *+36* mv. So far as is known, he never had any subsequent seizures. This lone episode occurred one day after a solar eclipse, and was associated with comparable field-strength intensifications in other subjects.

iii. Ovulation

iv. Premenstrual tension states (e.g., Subject B77, Figs. 16a and 16b)

v. Pregnancy

vi. Alertness, arousal, sudden spurts of energy, stimuli other than sudden fright (see Burr et al.)

vii. Fatigue in those showing relatively sustained voltage intensifications.

(c) Changes in statefunction principally involving the **E** quantity, preceded by or associated with field shifts to low intensification, the polar direction of which appears to be conditioned by individuated electrocyclic variables:

  i. Drowsiness, sleep, lack of stimuli, repose (see Burr et al.)
  ii. Hypoxia or hypercapnea and gaseous anesthetics (see Burr et al.)
  iii. Typical hypnosis tracings
  iv. Coma
  v. Aging in adults
  vi. Fatigue

(d) Changes in statefunction principally involving the **H** quantity, preceded by or associated with field shifts in the plus direction:

  i. Recovery from illness or from gastrointestinal or allergic symptoms
  ii. Migraine*
  iii. Sudden fear or startle responses (e.g., subject 157)
  iv. Youth

The relativity of **E** and **H** field quantities at once becomes evident. For example, zero and hi-minus readings may indicate alertness or drowsiness or fatigue at any given time depending on the direction, magnitude and rate of change. Despite such variables, some of the serious somatic disorders characteristically occurring in older age groups have been correlated with relatively sustained hi-minus values.

* Although severe headaches in subjects with histories of migraine have been correlated with high magnitudes of plus or minus polarity, in the four subjects whose voltage gradients were plotted during an actual migraine episode, including atypical migraines, the polarity has been uniformly plus. If verified, this may explain the known facts that migraine symptoms tend to disappear with aging and commence after or during adolescence.

3

Relatively sudden field intensifications can signal not only emotional disturbances but also physical symptoms that are apt to appear after hi-minus intensifications. In those who experience emotional or thinking problems at EMF intensifications of either plus or minus polarity, hi-minus polarity can be associated with a great variety of "psychosomatic" manifestations.

It is suggested that diseases such as influenza or even head colds can trigger associated anxieties or perturbations in those who suffer from them when EMF intensifications are high. Similarly, during hi-minus field intensifications, emotions can precipitate physical disorders.

Somatic disease resistance seems to depend on field intensification in the plus direction. Thus, an individual exhibiting anxiety while his field intensifications are moving in the plus direction when he is suffering from a bad head cold may not lose his anxiety while his head cold improves because, as he moves to hi-plus, his anxieties or fears are likely to increase.

This explains a phenomenon which some of us have experienced, however emotionally stable we may be. After recovering from a bad cold or influenza, one may feel unreasonably depressed for some days. One may perhaps also suffer from insomnia when recovering from an illness because insomnia has been correlated with hi-plus EMFs, particularly in the late night and early morning hours.

In illness associated with fever, exaggerated diurnal field shifts correlate with the characteristic body temperature cycle—the patient's temperature tending to be lowest in the early morning hours (typically in the plus direction of the field) and highest in the late afternoon and/or early evening hours (usually in the minus direction of the field). This, however, varies somewhat from day to day, lunation to lunation, season to season, year to year and person to person.

EMF correlates of unusually vivid dreams and field intensification in the plus direction show rhythmic variations as well as frequent appearance just before or during recovery from illness.

4

Field measurements may explain otherwise mysterious attractions or aversions between two individuals at given time intervals. While measuring the EMFs of nursing personnel and other controls at Pennsylvania Hospital and University of Pennsylvania Medical School in 1955-1958, it was discovered that when two persons were fighting both showed high intensified EMFs of either plus or minus polarity. Fights and arguments occurred particularly at hi-plus. In the very few instances measured when one individual was accelerating in the plus direction and the other in the minus, the two seemed strongly attracted to each other at that given instant.

When this happens to two individuals, the results can be dramatic. If, while subject to this intense attraction between fields, they decide to plunge into a precipitous marriage, the results can be disastrous since their states are continuously changing in time.

This explains something which most people have experienced in the course of their lives. They have been attracted to someone but when they met again a few weeks later they could not imagine what they had "seen" in each other.

A striking example of such a strong attraction was observed by the author and the episode might well be entitled, "Love on a Millivoltmeter." On November 10, 1978, an acquaintance, accompanied by her friend, came in for EMF measurements both at noon and in the evening. At noon, her notations on rating scales from 1 to 8 read: wonderful to bad—*2* (nearly wonderful), lethargic to energetic—*4* (in between), irritable to not irritable—*3* (slightly irritable), silent to talkative—*3* (slightly silent), hostile to sociable—6 (just less than maximal sociability), depressed to elated—*4* (in between), good physical state to bad physical state—*3* (better than average). The grid electrode was placed on the forehead and the ground electrode on one of her palms. She went into a spontaneous trance state as indicated by pupillary dilation, ocular fixation, and eye-blink reflex loss.

As soon as the recording began, her initial electrometric reading of +*28* mv had already begun to detensify, reaching the zero line at about 12:03 p.m. Soon her EMF intensified +*7* mv and then detensified to +*4* mv, following which she suddenly moved next to her friend on the couch and put her hand on his shoulder. This correlated with intensifications to +*20* mv which gradually decreased, developing the straight-line hypnotic configuration which slowly crossed the zero line, reversing polarity to -*5* mv.

Suddenly she exclaimed to her friend, "I just love you to death!" Almost immediately the field recording accelerated to zero, intensifying and detensifying in bursts of fast activity of varying frequency, averaging from +*4* to +*36* mv and lasting about two and a half minutes, Fig. 29a. Following this, the voltage gradient detensified in a straight-line pattern, at first rapidly, then slowly until a baseline of -*2* mv was recorded. At this point, she impulsively kissed her companion, with an accompanying voltage excursion to -*11* mv followed by similar bursts of high voltage fast activity ranging from 0 to +*36* mv, this episode lasting about the same length of time as that of her preceding dramatic outburst. Again the voltage gradient detensified rapidly, though very low voltage fast frequencies persisted in what otherwise might have represented a deeper hypnotic straight-line pattern, Fig. 29a.

In the next unillustrated sequence, after shifting from deeper to lighter trance states, the subject pulled out a cassette recorder to tape the remaining session. Just before this monitoring ended at 12:38 p.m., during a precipitous voltage upsurge from *+8* to *+24* mv, she suddenly asked about another woman acquaintance, showing considerable jealousy. In the noon session, during a plus electrometric baseline state, most emotive episodes correlated with voltage excursions into plus polarity.

For the evening session, the subject appeared with the same male friend and, as before, with a cassette recorder, blaring background music throughout the monitoring which I also taped on another recorder. In the evening, she signed her rating scale as "BITCH." Rating-scale notations were as follows: wonderful to bad—*4* (in between or worse than morning), lethargic to energetic—*3* (more lethargic or slightly more so than morning), irritable to not irritable—*3* (slightly irritable, or same as morning), silent to talkative—*4* (in between and slightly more talkative than morning), hostile to sociable—*4* (in between but more hostile than morning), depressed or elated—*3* (slightly depressed and slightly more depressed than morning), good physical state to bad physical state (left unmarked).

Field monitoring began at 9:22 p.m. The baseline reading showed unusual head-palm intensifications of minus polarity*—fast spiky waves varying from *-27* to *-9* mv with a sharp downward excursion to *-33* mv immediately preceding a straight-line hypnotic detensification to *-22* mv, development of low voltage faster frequencies to *-27* mv, a sudden detensification to *-22* mv, a rapid intensification to *-34* mv, followed by a gradual straight-line detensification to *-24* mv. This was followed by another episode of fast frequencies ranging from *-12* to *-34* mv, which at 9:24 p.m. was recorded at *-19* mv, Fig. 29b.

---

* Field monitoring with head-palm leads usually shows the head positive to the palm.

During the relatively long interval of voltage decrease, the subject again developed a spontaneous trance state with visual fixation on the recording of her changing voltage pattern. Her friend then spoke of her being transferred to another city, his comments suddenly punctuated by her response in a much deeper voice:

Subject: I'm in control of the situation. (This was shortly followed by a remark in a more natural voice). But (laughs) I *would* like to marry you (laughs). But you're the only one I want. Ummmm ahh (impulsively kissing her friend again.) Ummmm ahhh! (laughs).

Friend: (indicating the recording) Look at that. Look at that! (softly).

Subject: I'll go down to 50...(*-50* mv).

Friend: Hi-plus today and negative tonight. It's amazing.

Subject: It is, isn't it—when you stop and think about it.

Friend: Yes, it is. It reverses polarity beautifully. I betcha hi-plus.

Subject: Wanna try it?

Friend: No, wait till you—calm down a little bit—get it down as close to zero as possible.

After the kiss, her minus polarity field measurements rapidly intensified from *-19* to *-30* mv. As her hypnotic state deepened over the next nine minutes, the measurements gradually detensified in a straight-line pattern until 9:29 p.m. At that point, a rapid intensification from -2 to *-28* mv occurred, again with the development of short bursts of fast frequencies varying from -22 to -32 mv.

During this voltage flux the subject sobbed: "Ahh...ahh...I can't bear the thought of you (sic) leaving me (sic) (sobbing)...Ahh...Oooohhh ..." (almost simultaneously sobbing and laughing).

A deeper hypnotic state then developed with detensification to -22 mv. At this point the experiment ended at 9:31 p.m., Fig. 29b.

While it could easily have been assumed that the subject's histrionic comments and actions represented only yet another over-done act for which she was famous, the dramatic, episodic voltage excursions indicate profound feelings. These intensified into the minus side of the scale from her evening minus baseline state—the opposite of her plus baseline state at noon with most emotive excursions being in a higher plus range.

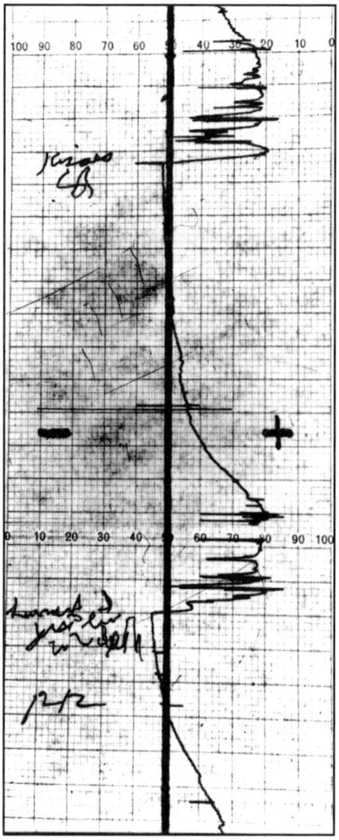

FIG. 29a. (read from bottom to top) Noon field tracing of spontaneous hypnotic states with emotive outbursts of variable fast frequency, plus polarity intensifications, November 10, 1978.

After noting the subject's unusual minus baseline state and her friend's earlier comment to the subject that his own baseline pattern would be of plus polarity, it was necessary to check the friend's earlier prediction. At 9:38 p.m., his initial +*36* mv measurement slowly detensified in a nonhypnotic waking state pattern to +22 mv, which occurred at 9:43 p.m.

5

To summarize, one example of electrodynamic field monitoring of recurring spontaneous trance states with emotive perturbations is herewith documented. As previously demonstrated since 1948, emotions have been equated with measurable energy.

This also illustrates the typical diurnal field shifts from plus to minus polarity, most of the emotional thoughts and subsequent outbursts being recorded in the plus polarity range at noon and in the minus polarity range in the evening.

These sudden and violent electric attractions are often mistaken for "love at first sight" and sometimes, perhaps, other factors being favorable, they have led to a satisfactory permanent relationship. But couples will be well advised to realize that electric attractions are not necessarily "love" and that it is a good plan to allow a few weeks for their fields to stabilize before they make legal decisions about each other.

Such electric attractions or aversions can occur between individuals of the same sex with no apparent sexual factors involved. It is a good plan, therefore, for all of us to be aware of them. If, for example, we feel an intense dislike for someone we meet, we should remember that in a week or two, when our mutual fields have settled down, we may find that the other is not such a bad individual as we had thought.

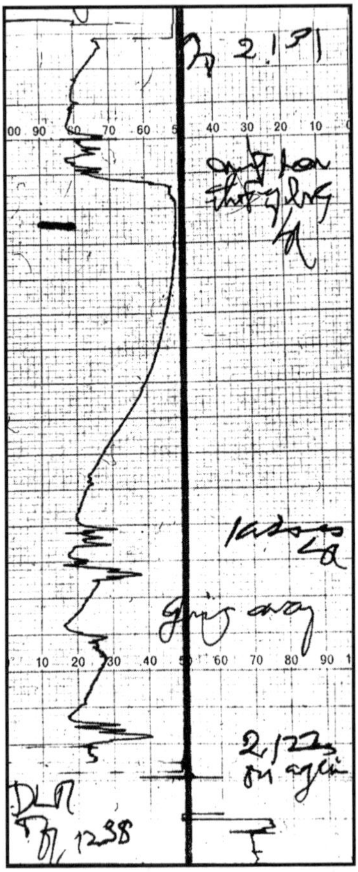

FIG. 29b. (read from bottom to top) Evening field tracing of spontaneous hypnotic states showing diurnal field shifts from plus to minus polarity with emotive outbursts recorded in the minus polarity range.

6

As previously discussed, human state changes correlate with electromagnetic field variations which are related to seasonal and other periodicities. In the northern hemisphere the maximal plus intensifications tend to occur in December and January—the maximal minus voltage swings occurring in the spring or summer.

Curious deviations from the seasonal electrocyclic pattern have been noted during certain years and in certain subjects. For example, during the winter of 1955-1956 in Philadelphia, head-chest polarities tended to be minus throughout November and December, reaching their plus maxima in mid-January. On the other hand, manic-depressive patient 219 reached her plus maximum in late November. Subjects having spring allergies or gastrointestinal exacerbations during this season tend to show minus maxima during March, May or June. Furthermore, Subject 170, one of the persons periodically monitored since 1948, who was allergic to giant ragweed, and who tended to show relatively hi-minus field configurations during the autumn hay fever season, was symptom-free in the fall of 1961. As might be expected, the ragweed count remained relatively low throughout this period. Yet his field intensities had been plotted in the plus range long before hay fever season, and intermittent readings during this season suggested that if anything, his voltage gradients were showing intensification in the plus direction.

Despite such variations, however, electrocyclic periodicities have recurred with remarkable consistency year after year in different subjects measured at different points in the United States.

Variations within diurnal and fortnightly cycles—the latter approximating full and new moon—appear to be conditioned by their temporal positions within monthly and seasonal periods. In the fall and winter, maximal positivity tends to occur around new moon and less positive or minus voltage excursions around full moon. For example, Fig. 30 illustrates the daily field plots of Subject 210, a twenty-seven-year-old schizophrenic patient, at new and full moon in January 1956, as compared with combined daily field means of thirty-six patients and controls who were simultaneously measured, and with the subject's predictions of her readings. Concerning her divergent guesses on January 28, one was based on how she felt and the other on what she thought the millivoltmeter would record.

Table 11 exemplifies the daily mean field shifts of ten randomly selected subjects before, during and after the January new moon depicted in Fig. 30. Corresponding verbatim comments concerning changes in statefunction are included to show the highly individuated feelings: cues, language symbols and, where present, somatic events or symptoms associated with such changing field patterns.

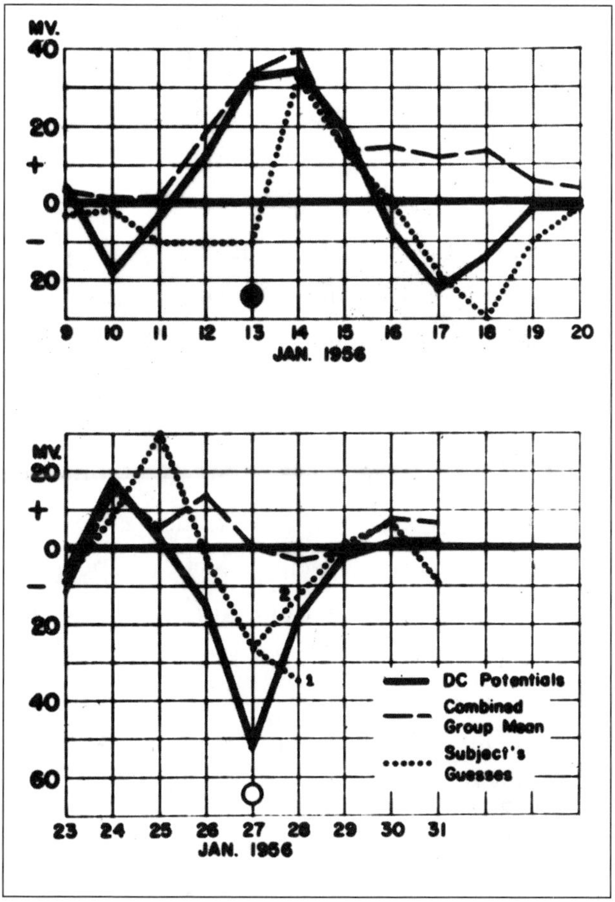

FIG. 30. Algebraic mean daily field measurements of chronic undifferentiated schizophrenic patient 210, showing typical January sinusoidal polar reversals at new and full moon followed by symptom exacerbations, as compared with combined daily field means of thirty-six patients and controls, and patient 210's guesses of her changing feeling states relative to **E** and **H** field quantities.(Published in L. J. Ravitz: History, measurement, and applicability of periodic changes in the electromagnetic field in health and disease. *An. NY Acad. Sc.* 98 1144-1201, 1962.)

Briefly, like the fortnightly cycles, diurnal variations show expansions, contractions and polar reversals scattered throughout the year depending in part on the season and the fortnightly period. Pronounced morning-evening variations tend to occur in December-January and June-July, especially in persons undergoing state perturbations such as depressions. For example, during a month of relative field quiescence, August 1948, only one subject who was recovering from a depressive episode showed significant diurnal shifts.

It is of interest to note that certain of the described periodicities appear on inspection to correspond with certain geomagnetic variations. Further, the previously mentioned parallelisms between periodic movements in different forms of life as well as between earth, atmosphere and tree voltage gradients, provide further evidence for the primacy of an exogenous component regulating electrocyclic timing. Additionally, the annual cycle which is present in trees roughly parallels the sunspot cycle. Effects of specific terrestrial variables, such as latitude, on the timings of individual clinical manifestations require detailed exploration. Although it is difficult to compare different human subjects measured at latitudes ranging from New Haven, Connecticut, to Daytona Beach, Florida; longitudes as far west as North Chicago, Illinois and elevations varying from sea level to 1000 feet or more, the field strengths of the same patients and controls measured in Philadelphia by the same instrument showed significant contractions in 1956-1957 relative to comparable periods in 1955-1956. Hence, it may be worth noting that in 1954-1955, the field strengths of both disturbed schizophrenic patients and controls measured in North Chicago and Philadelphia showed values averaging 25 to 50% less than those of similar groups measured with the same instrument over corresponding periods during 1950-1951 in Durham, North Carolina and Salem, Virginia.

TABLE 11

COMPARISONS BETWEEN DAILY MEAN FIELD SHIFTS OF RANDOMLY SELECTED CONTROLS AND PATIENTS AND THEIR COMMENTS RECORDED IMMEDIATELY FOLLOWING READINGS, UNIVERSITY OF PENNSYLVANIA MEDICAL SCHOOL, PHILADELPHIA, PA, JANUARY 1956.

Showing exacerbations and remissions of general state perturbations, periods of unusually vivid dreams, ineffable feelings, depressions, ovulation, bloating, epistaxis, menstrual symptoms, insomnia, drowsiness, dissimulation and migraine; 61 measurements of 10 subjects before, during and after lunar conjunction. (Numbers in parentheses denote hospitalized patients; ..... denotes omitted daily readings.)

Subject	Day, date, E and 11 means (mv) and lunation													
	W 1/11—n_{-2}		Th 1/12—n_{-1}		F 1/13—n_0		Sa 1/14—n_{+1}		Su 1/15—n_{+2}		M 1/16—n_{+3}		Tu 1/17—n_{+4}	
	E	**H**	**E**	**H**	**E**	**H**	**E**	**H**	**E**	**H**	**E**	**H**	**E**	**H**
170 ♂	4 Optimum.	*+4*	0 O.K.	*0*	27 Very vivid dreams last night; premature wakening; funny feeling in head; excited; very active.	*+27*	23 Still keyed up though less so.	*+23*	12 Less excited.	*+12*	11 Slightly excited.	*+11*	20 Keyed up and miffed.	*+20*
189 ♂	0 Feel like zero.	*0*	0 Feel like zero.	*0*	34 This is the feeling-in-the-head day; not an affect; just a subjective sensation engrafted on a +20.	*+34*	37 Sensation which can only be described in terms of what machine means—plussy.[a]	*+37*	.....		0 Good and relaxed; no feeling in head.	*0*	15 Felt zero, but noted startle reaction when wife slammed door.	*+15*
192 ♂	.....		27 More depressed tremulous; very tired; vivid recurring dream last night.	*+27*	30 Wife noted peculiar mood last night; still up.	*+30*	89 Feel as bad today as I ever did; want to withdraw from enviroment.[b]	*+89*	.....		28 I'm still under influence of whatever this mysterious force is.	*+28*	37 More depressed today.	*+37*
(210) ♀	4 Miserable, not as withdrawn; complately impatient and edgy.	*-4*	15 Edgy today.	*+15*	34 (Ovulation) Mid-abdominal tightening.[c]	*+34*	35 (Ovulation) Mid-abdominal tightening.[d]	*+35*	19 Less anguish.	*+19*	8 (No comments)[e]	*-8*	22 Tight, not tense and withdrawn,but wanting not to be withdrawn; worried; frightened.[f]	*-22*

[illegible] ♀	[illegible] (Nosebleed). Feel closer to people.	[illegible] (Nosebleed). No subjective change.	[illegible] (Nosebleed). Energetic; good; keyed up; happy; euphoric.	Same. [g]	Feeling better.	Fine.	Fine.
(223) ♀	0 *0* No special comments.	17 *+17* I've given my doctor too much, and must protect myself.	24 *+2* (Ovulation). Feel like throwing things.	35 *+35* (Menstrual period started). Tense.	. . . . . (In bed with menstrual cramps).	19 *+19* Mad at myself.	11 *+11* Better today; less depressed; not worried how I'm to react today.
224 ♂	2 *+2* Calm; feel good.	20 *+20* Worried; very tired.	40 *+40* Insomnia last night (rare); thinking of things; unusually vivid dream last night; depressed. [h]	. . . . . (Out of town) . . .		0 *0* Relaxed spirits higher; much more energetic.	5 *-5* Very sleepy; almost obsessional getting things done today which I had let go.
225 ♂	26 *+26* Keyed up although things went well today.	13 *+13* Less tense; less insecure; more relaxed.	77 *+77* Unusually tired this morning; not tense. [i]	82 *+82* Not tired in morning. [j]	62 *+62* As tense as I've been; in a great hurry.	15 *+9* Much more relaxed; almost optimum.	1 *+1* In good relaxed shape.
226 ♂	. . . . .	10 *+10* O.K.	50 *+50* Mad today; couldn't get a joke today.	47 *+47* Tired; blew up; irritable.	35 *+35* Mad as hell.	12 *+12* Not angry.	69 *+69* Fell asleep at gathering. [k]
228 ♀	17 *-17* Contrary to everything and everybody and mad at everyone; horrible mood; as evil as I can get.	5 *-5* Much better; still not optimum.	39 *+39* Awoke at 7:30 a.m. with terrific migraine; could hardly open eyes; vomiting; intense pain.	. . . . . (In bed with migraine)		25 *+25* (No comments).	0 *0* Life's worth living again.

n=new moon.
a Overtalkative all day according to wife, who accompanied him.
b Standing staring into space; difficulty articulating.
c Within 2 hours after measurements, patient had a panic reaction.
d Pacing floor.
e Slight bloating of face.
f Increasing bloating of face.
g Later, patient reported that she did not feel well, possibly depressed.
h Insomnia the following evening.
i Closed eyes during readings.
j Became very tense before bedtime the following evening.
k Flushed but appeared jocular and laughed frequently. On 2/8/56, he spontaneously admitted feeling very depressed on 1/17/56.

(Published in L. J. Ravitz: History, measurement, and appalicability of periodic change in the electromagnetic field in the health and disease. *An NY Acad. Sc.* 98: 1144-1201, 1962.)

In any event, to date the only living systems measured in which electrocyclic phenomena show relative loss of rhythmicity and/or apparently delayed periodic movements of varying frequency are some of the chronic schizophrenics *in states of relative exhaustion,* and the single case of post-encephalitic basal ganglia encephalopathy which, thus far, has been monitored. Likewise, such apparent breakdowns could conceivably occur in certain senile patients. On the other hand, as might be expected, electrocyclic phenomena persisted in two schizophrenic patients after undergoing, respectively, a bimedial lobotomy and a thalamotomy.

7

In several pilot studies, various empiric predictions have been made for individuals, based on the electrocyclic patterns. Thus far, these have been based principally on the following considerations:

i) Predictions of state perturbations within twelve hours of accelerated field intensifications with subtle clinical signs of increasing disturbance

After several months of participation in an experimental rehabilitation program, patient 142, a thirty-one-year-old chronic catatonic schizophrenic patient who showed occasional episodes of disturbed behavior, was considered dramatically improved in every sphere. On March 24, at a discriminatory, integrative level of functioning, his voltage gradients averaged +*5* mv. The next day, personnel in the control building where he resided likewise rated him as functioning relatively optimally. His measurements, however, had accelerated in the plus direction and now averaged +*111* mv with greater variability. Although still pleasant and casually jocular, he seemed unusually curious about the electrodes which were the same pair that had been used to plot his field quantities since August. Moreover, at times he showed subtle, involuntary muscle movements; displayed transitory catalepsy of the eyelids, and on examination, catalepsy of both upper extremities; and exuded a peculiar, pungent body odor which, in him, characteristically occurred at hi-plus intensifications. Within four hours, on the baseball field, patient 142 suddenly became assaultive and incontinent and exhibited marked disorganization of speech. The following day, however, his field strength had dropped to a mean of *+63* mv, a 48-mv shift within 24 hours, and he was much improved.

(ii) Predictions of state perturbations within eighteen hours of accelerated field intensifications without any clinical signs of increasing disturbance

In the early morning hours of June 29, twenty-four hours prior to a solar eclipse, the field means of Subject 172, a thirty-seven-year-old man with a history of peptic ulcers, read *-91* mv, 91 mv from a zero mean during his last measurements and the highest field intensification ever recorded on him. He felt as fine as he had at his previous reading. Late the following afternoon, about eighteen hours later, he noted extreme irritability, fatigue, with multiple vivid dreams the night before, a rare occurrence since he seldom remembered dreaming, and he had a tight feeling in his head which bothered him to the extent that he held it between measurements. He could hardly get out of bed earlier in the day because he was so logy, and was unable to indicate whether he felt depressed. Voltage means were now *-21* mv. On June 31, at another hi-minus spike, -51 mv, he was even more dragging and languid, although he had an easier time getting out of bed earlier in the day. Not until July 1 did subject 172 begin to feel more energetic and cheerful (*-18* mv). Over this span of time, his wife and child showed comparable field patterns.

(iii) Predictions of state perturbations within eight hours of presumed accelerated field intensifications without measuring the subject, by noting marked accelerations of a specific direction in other subjects and knowing

that symptom exacerbations occur in this particular subject at high intensifications of this direction

The symptoms of patient 211, a twenty-four-year-old schizophrenic patient, tended to show exacerbations in the late afternoon or early evening hours, coinciding with her typical diurnal field shifts from low-minus (i.e., relatively plus) to hi-minus configurations. At those times, the diurnal rhythm underwent polar reversals, her symptom exacerbations and remissions, likewise, were reversed. Furthermore, she was at her best in the winter months during those periods of group voltage intensification in the plus direction. Although frequently tense and jittery as she maintained levels in the low-plus range, it was at least a welcome relief from the marked depersonalization she felt at her typically hi-minus configuration. Moreover, at her excursions into low-plus values, which were seldom maintained over any appreciable period, her entire countenance underwent a profound change: the characteristic rigidity of her facial muscles dissolved, leaving a much softer configuration, her mouth was no longer drawn and her voice and gait developed a timbre and springiness which made her appear years younger. At hi-minus readings, on the other hand, her physiognomy became mask-like, and she often exhibited the so-called corrugator phenomenon, a special type of dissociation limited to the region above the nose bridge between the eyebrows. On March 30, patient 211 was considered sufficiently improved by her two psychoanalysts to venture downtown, hence was not monitored on that day. However, profound minus accelerations soon were noted in most of the remaining patients and controls beginning in the early afternoon. The nursing supervisor was notified that a possibility existed that patient 211 would show marked symptoms when she returned that evening, and a memorandum was sent to the principal psychiatric consultant. The previous morning she had felt relatively well (0 mv), but by evening had shifted her feeling scale to depressed, detached and exhausted (-*25* mv). When she was seen later in the evening of March 30 following her return to the hospital, she was profoundly depersonalized and panic-stricken (-*54* mv), symptoms which improved somewhat by the following morning (-*20* mv).

8

Statefunction in less differentiated life forms can be altered and controlled by superimposing appropriate external fields without recourse to complex chemical reactions, metabolic gradients and other derivative processes.

On the other hand, the control of future states in human samples poses a difficult task since field strengths across cell membranes 20 to 50 A thick have been calculated to average 300,000 to 500,000 volts/cm, considering the phase boundaries between nucleus and cytoplasm, mitochondria and other elements. To be sure, various agents such as x-rays, gamma rays, and even electroshock and diathermy affect human field properties. Aside from the destructive potentialities of most of these procedures, affecting fundamental processes is scarcely synonymous with the control.

Chapter Fourteen

RANDOM REFLECTIONS

1

The Burr-Northrop *Electro-Dynamic Theory of Life* embraces all forms of life and has important implications for those concerned in many diverse areas, from psychiatry and medicine to agriculture and earthquake predictions, the military and space travel.

Possible future applications of the electrodynamic field theory include the following:

1. Utilizing field measurements as a predictive supplement in psychiatric and medical cases, including cancer, e.g., prostate, breast and genito urinary system.
2. Extending the use of field measurements to predict ovulation—preventing and/or enhancing conception.
3. Understanding and treating disease, psychiatric disorders and the effects of aging in terms of basic field forces.
4. Changing the electrodynamic fields of the body, through self-hypnosis, to improve individual emotional and physical states.
5. Monitoring electrodynamic fields of trees, atmosphere and earth at varying distances from specific fault lines as a possible tool for predicting earthquakes.
6. Predicting hurricanes through procedures similar to the above.
7. Assessing times when expensively-trained military personnel will be best and least able to cope with stress.
8. Comparing astronauts' field measurements on earth and dur-

ing space travel for optimal performance levels.

9. Developing supplementary diagnostic classifications in psychiatry and medicine based on field intensity, **E** and polarity, **H** quantities at given times, emphasizing the time factor as a crucial variable in medical, psychiatric and psychologic assessments.
10. Employing field measurements in assessing the states of prisoners and patients considered for parole or discharge, especially in predicting potential violence.
11. Using field measurements in agriculture to predict the best seeds to plant.
12. Determining the pathogenicity of bacteria and viruses.

Different strains of a number of species of microbial pathogens are known to differ in their pathogenicity or virulence. These differences can sometimes be attributed to differences in capacity to produce known virulence factors such as toxins. On the other hand, there are many instances of differences in virulence which cannot at the present time be attributed to any known virulence factor. It might be interesting in both cases to attempt to determine whether strains exhibiting differences in virulence also differ in their electromagnetic properties. One must be cautious in conducting such experiments because each bacterial colony contains thousands to millions of individual cells. One must also be cautious because observed potential differences may not be causally related to virulence.

2

The field theory demolishes any attempt to reduce field properties to chemistry and forces on those faithful to old concepts the shattering conclusion that the atoms and molecules of chemistry, in fact the entire concept of valence, reduce to electricity, and in this specific instance, to quantum fields.

To be sure, in these experiments, the molecules involved comprise a complex of several types of voltage gradients which naturally involve oxidative metabolism. However, chemical reactions provide the fuel but are not the engine; they cannot give direction and represent a degradation of energy. Electromagnetic fields, on the other hand, have the vector property necessary both to establish and give direction to unit charges within their ranges. Margenau regards them as electric "signposts" to guide the flow of energy in the system. As they indicate, too, the stored energy available for activity, Burr regarded them as a measurement of the vital capacity of any organism to store, mobilize and direct energy—an indication of the capacity of any creature to adjust to its physical and ideational environment.

The *Theory* thus harmonizes biologic systems with the laws of the universe. It shows that every living system is organized and actuated by a dynamic pattern, that both organic and inorganic systems represent the expression of an electromagnetic field. As points on continuum, in ways both explicable and rational, living and nonliving forms finally can take their places in the organization of the universe.

3

In an age in which many boast of the "conquest of nature" it is salutary to reflect that we can neither dominate nor pin down the fields on which our very existence depends; fields refuse to be netted or neatly pigeonholed. While they operate the nervous system and other structures, they are not confined to them nor unalterably associated with any specific arrangement of nerve units. We cannot make any mechanical model of the field nor portray it in those cute little diagrams with boxes so beloved by many scientists.

Local field disturbances are influenced by the state of the total field at any given point, while the state of the total field is influenced by local perturbations. The total field, however, always maintains its prime dominance and therefore there is no complete reciprocity. This fact promises to simplify problems in biology, the behavior sciences and medicine without exclusively considering complex arrangements of particles. It provides new shortcuts to understanding the basic forces of aging as well as to physical and behavior disorders because the ebb and flow of these are inseparably fused to electrocyclic phenomena.

Emotional perturbations can now be viewed in a new light—as variations in the balance between the evolutionary ancient brain core and the recently evolved neocortex; behavior disquietudes are related to the varying, unstable functioning of the cortex which fluctuates under field-strength intensifications and detensifications from *states of excitation* to *states of exhaustion*.

Even hypnosis is now seen, in part, to be a natural field phenomenon. It involves shifts in the balance between the ancient brain core and the neocortex—shifts which produce changes in the total field.

4

Not unnaturally, the relativity principles on which these investigations are based still tend to evoke blank looks in those traditionally or temperamentally compelled to "think" in terms of magically fixed correlates of empirically denoted entities. Yet reproducible measures of relative changes in statefunction conform to the operations of nature. For nature seems impishly delighted to bypass clinical pigeonholes and equip her creatures with continuous variations; she endows them with the need for wider varieties of stimulation as the role of the neocortex becomes more prominent.

The Burr-Northrop *Electro-Dynamic Theory of Life* helps us to understand nature's whims; it provides, in part, the basic organization, or matrix, of all living forms and allows us to perceive and to measure some of nature's capers.

Perturbations in the field indicate disturbances in the system, though the field profile itself does not indicate the nature of the disturbance. Then, with man's functioning neocortex, complicating factors are superimposed on the internal driving force with its periodic movements.

Less complex vertebrates with less neocortical equipment and with no language symbols are immune from the disturbing effects of the neocortically-trapped cultural or moral imperatives reverberating in many of their more evolved human cousins. So they can conduct themselves more spontaneously and in accord with their ancient feelings.

In other words, in machines, whether nature's or man-made, the more complex the design, the greater the potential difficulties. More things can go wrong in less time-proved organizations. Since structure preceded function in the nervous system and evolved long before it began to show signs of function, it follows that the recently evolved neocortical cells are more fragile and unstable than those of the ancient brain core. They are more subject to the ravages of time as well as to toxins and emotional excitations.

5

Any scientific theory, to be valid, must have certain qualities which have been expressed by both Margenau and Northrop. The Burr-Northrop electrodynamic field theory is the first in biology to meet Margenau's three principal "metaphysical requirements" for any fertile scientific theory, the most important of which are: *(a) simplicity, (b) extensibility* and *(c) causality.*

The Burr-Northrop *Theory* is based on a monistic principle involving (1) *definition* of state (2) *prediction* of future states and (3) *control* of future states.

Such monism meets Margenau's first two requirements of (a) *simplicity* and (b) *extensibility* far better than contemporary pluralistic theories. The final major requirement (c) *causality,* is satisfied in principle because the *Theory* can relate different uniquely determinable states of one's subject matter at different times to a unique definition of state at any given time. It follows that *The Electro-Dynamic Theory of Life* is the first to provide foundations for future mathematical causality in both the behavior and medical spheres.

6

Thus, thousands of experiments have reinforced without contradiction the primacy of the field, the measurement of which can provide crucial invariant scientific data in many diverse areas of critical importance.

Chapter Fifteen

Summary and Conclusions

1

As a primary property of nature, then, the electrodynamic or electromagnetic field represents one of the most basic factors. Until the fourth decade of the past century, however, the importance of fields in living systems was not recognized for two reasons. First, prior to 1935, measuring instruments tended to draw current from the creature being measured and could not reliably indicate pure voltage gradients. Second, there existed not only naive assumptions about fields but also a general pre-relativity preoccupation with, as Northrop so aptly put it:

> ...false 'particle-physics' interpretations of rectilinear-moving-and-permuting, feelingless, atomic billiard-balls-through-holes-in-Swiss-cheese theory of everything, which of course is as much rubbish in Newton's mechanics as in Maxwell's electromagnetics.

Since those days, years of careful experimentation with sensitive instruments and special electrodes have demonstrated not only local phenomena but phenomena at loci distal to the electrode placements. For example, field measurements of such apparently disparate phenomena as ovulation and malignancy can be detected from distant positions in the same system, because the whole is affected by local events. Moreover, field quantities can also be measured from points outside the organism either through a salt-water medium—as in the salamander experiment—or even through the air which is a poor conducting medium. This was exemplified by the bullfrog sciatic nerve experiment noted in Chapters 3 and 4.

Since field measurements involve the entire organism, can be plotted at varying distances from it and disappear at death, it is obvious that they are basic phenomena. They exist even in unfertilized eggs, remain constant despite the complex chemical changes accompanying fertilization and predict longitudinal axes and the subsequent development of embryos after fertilization has occurred.

Although the dominant center of the polarized field fails to reveal any fixed point or structure—and no classic model of it can be constructed with respect to traditional mechanics—certain aspects are peripherally measurable in units of energy. Notwithstanding, the fixed, diversified structural units of the nervous system define certain field functions—discrete subcortical entities contributing to the development of transient, relatively slowly shifting field configurations, dynamic patterns of performance as a whole operating through, though neither confined within nor inflexibly associated with, any specific arrangement of the nervous elements. Thus, although clinical correlates suggest that while in operation some of these processes are both structurally-functionally and spatially-temporally localizable, radiating as they do through a nonspecific non-nervous matrix, electromagnetic field properties may utilize any appropriate tissues or structures at hand without significant changes in pattern. It follows that the configuration of any phenomenon is not necessarily dependent on the geometry of any stable structure, arising only under appropriate circumstances and potentially capable of operating through different sets of nervous connections on each occasion.

Furthermore, continuing attempts to reduce electromagnetic fields to properties of individual particles within any living thing are predicated on the traditional belief that there is sensible meaning for the concept of potentials at a point. The fictitious nature of this assumption has been amply demonstrated by Gibbs' analysis of the electric properties of solutions; as well as through the experimental findings of Harned, Taylor, Guggenheim and Teorell. Again, there exist no absolute reference points in any form of life—only motion. Even polarity is determined only by the specific geometry of electrode placements, and hence is entirely a relative matter.

2

Such relativity likewise extends to the epistemic operational, or instrumental definitions of electrodynamic, electromagnetic and quasi-electrostatic fields, terms which can now be used interchangeably. In other words, the important point concerns the fact that fields are being measured; any real distinctions are those determined by the instruments utilized in making the measurements. This, of course, highlights the glaring insufficiency of every monolithic theory of definitions to the obvious dismay of those impelled to think in terms of absolute unitary, concrete conceptions of "reality" which have been replaced in all branches of physics. To be sure, constitutive definitions cannot be rejected. But to have any fertile meaning, the epistemic or operational definitions also must be present. And in the case of fields, ignorance of different types of definitions completely obscures the fundamental interrelatedness of different aspects of the same thing.

To distinguish these fields from alternating current (AC) recordings [the rapidly fluctuating currents as are found in the heart (electrocardiogram) and brain (electroencephalogram)], they are often called "DC fields," "DC potential differences," or "DC voltage gradients." Such nomenclature, however, has resulted in considerable confusion, since DC implies direct current flow. Electromagnetic field phenomena, on the other hand, do not involve current flow, comprising relatively steady state voltage gradients which change relatively slowly in space-time. Even at their highest value of 150,000 ohms, skin resistances cannot affect these field measurements.

Other erroneous implications have been drawn from the terms "bioelectric fields" and "force fields," the former perpetuating dualisms imputing a special kind of electricity in living matter, the latter evoking thoughts of static rather than dynamic fields. Russell coined the term "L-field" (Life-field) which, though appropriately descriptive of the electromagnetic fields of living systems, also implies a special field associated only with living matter.

Analogously, a reservoir of water represents a potential source of horsepower whether or not water is flowing from the reservoir. When water is drawn off to run a water wheel, current is flowing. Electromagnetic field experiments measure aspects of the equivalence of the head of water (the potential source of horsepower) and hence, have virtually nothing to do with the rate of water flow, that is, with current flow. It should be remembered that current is a function of these fields but that currents are more concerned with local events than electromagnetic fields, which likewise measure properties of the system as a whole.

The basic integrative functions of such fields have been established by Lund, Burr, Marsh and Beams and Anderson without considering various complex chemical interactions and metabolic gradients. Moreover, Lund has noted that hormonal action in plants is secondary to field phenomena which play a prime role in the spatial organization of metabolic processes. Further, the net effect of exogenous or endogenous alterations in the field are identical. Hence, all evidence indicates that electromagnetic fields act as phylogenetically primitive integrative factors, significant in such basic processes as morphogenesis and the establishment of symmetry in the absence of more recently derived nervous systems and hormonal action.

That the central nervous system with its polarized nervous elements participates in field phenomena and acts as a controlling agency in more differentiated creatures possessing such a structure is a long established fact. But what of the nervous and non-nervous controls? What of field phenomena in forms of life without a nervous system? Any analysis and reduction of the problem initiating inquiry to its most elemental factor compels consideration of basic forces actuating the design or pattern of living systems in general and of the nervous system in particular. That there exists directed design cannot be denied by any student of comparative embryology: forces must set up the longitudinal axis, control and regulate cell division, guide the ultimate differentiation of very young embryonic cells, determine where the cells are going to lie and direct nerve fibers communicating with nuclear masses. Feeling, behavior and thinking then follow as a consequence of design.

Brown's empiric investigations in biological cycles have resulted in his conclusion that "a new theory must be developed," although he erred in an opinion that there exists "no theory to explain" certain findings.

As we have seen in the foregoing pages, such a theory has not only existed since 1935 but has been confirmed by thousands of experiments.

3

In the preceding pages, we have made a preliminary study of a whole new branch of science—the nature and uses of the electrodynamic fields in living forms. Within the limits of a short book, it has only been possible to sketch some of the highlights of so vast a subject. It may be helpful, therefore briefly, to summarize what we have found:

1. Since 1935, when Burr and Northrop first proposed *The Electro-Dynamic Theory of Life* based on field physics, it has been possible to define the state of living matter in terms of multidimensional space-time and energy.

In the light of their *Theory*, new instruments and electrodes were invented to confirm by experiments, the existence of these electrodynamic fields in all living forms.

Maxwell's equations inspired the first Burr-Lane-Nims high-input impedance micro- and millivoltmeters which could screen out resistance and current flow and measure pure field physics variables using relational, reversible, nonpolarizing silver-silver chloride fluid-junction electrodes operating through a saline bridge (based on Gibbs' analysis of the electric properties of solutions) which do not disturb the system being studied.

2. This is the first known investigation wherein electrocyclic shifts have been objectively, quantitatively and reproducibly plotted on human subjects and shown to be identical to electrocyclic phenomena of other living systems in terms of basic electromagnetic field quantities, becoming more complex as one ascends the evolutionary tree. All are influenced by exogenous field rhythms of the environment.

This new approach, based on a monistic philosophy of science, fuses crucial time-factors or electrocyclic phenomena to the assessment of all living things. By knowing the statefunction of a given organism at a given time in the present, and by expecting similar state changes to recur at some given future time, it is theoretically possible to predict to some extent certain aspects of statefunction at given future times.

3. The first known objective, quantitative, reproducible metric

of hypnotic states has been devised. Confirming Erickson's empiric observations, it was found that hypnotic and autohypnotic states can be—and perhaps often are—independent of any hypnotist and are natural states of concentration which can be spontaneously developed and/or learned.

This finding destroys the value of many experiments on hypnotized versus nonhypnotized subjects, which neglect first to ascertain whether the subject is in a spontaneous trance state or simulating one.

4. The important experimental and therapeutic effects of hypnosis can now be shown to change the body's electromagnetic fields which can correlate with improved emotional and physical states.

5. Hypnotically revivified memories measured in the millivolt range are comparable to those revivified by Penfield when he stimulated the neocortex electrically, though these were not measured by him.

On the other hand, emotions revivified in hypnosis can be correlated with characteristic EMF changes as can the hypnotic state itself. Also, electroshock treatments revivified by hypnosis, produced characteristic convulsive EEG disruptions.

6. The time-dependent impact on the field of emotional ideas can be monitored. This is possible whether the emotions are detonated by present or past experience, spontaneous thoughts, illusions, dreams or even hallucinations in both nonhypnotic and hypnotic waking states, as well as in sleep, drugged states or gaseous inhalations.

7. Certain irreducible factors in the causation of behavior and somatic disorders have been discovered.

For the first known time in biology and medicine the crucial importance of polarized field quantities has been demonstrated in health, disease, injury, wound-healing, growth and aging.

Field changes have been found to precede—and perhaps to cause—perturbations in behavior and physical disorders. In the case of behavior perturbations, EMF intensifications are of either plus or minus polarity, favoring the intensity, **E** quantity. Physical disorders correlate with minus excursions, emphasizing the polarity, **H** vector. Both of these types of clinical manifestations can be correlated with one single regulating principle: changing field intensities and polarities which can be defined in relative terms and mapped objectively. Rather than "psyche" acting on "soma" and other such anthropomorphic, anthropocentric conceptions, both manifestations are postulated to result from changing intensities and directions of energy, *natural* energy which can be precisely but relatively defined and objectively recorded.

8. There is a dawning realization that many so-called "controlled" studies on living matter have scarcely been controlled because they fail to consider those crucial time variables—electrocyclic phenomena. These studies also indicate the limitations of most commonly accepted statistical methods as applied to living systems because they ignore the multidimensional, continuously changing states.

9. Field measurements make it possible to assess known periodicities in certain clinical conditions. In studies of patients and controls, several infectious diseases have been monitored. These observations have shown the importance of the polarity, **H** field quantity—unique to each individual as impacted by the environment.

10. Relatively sudden EMF intensifications correlate with subsequent development of state perturbations, somatic manifestations often appearing after hi-minus excursions. In those who experience disquietudes following either plus or minus EMF intensifications, the combined psychosomatic syndrome in the hi-minus

range can be associated with a wide variety of manifestations. Thus, the minus energy spin correlates of diseases such as influenza or even head colds can accompany perturbations in feeling, behavior or thinking. Similarly, during periodic hi-minus intensifications, the same energy spin can correlate with other physical disquietudes.

11. Resistance to somatic disease appears to be associated with EMF intensifications in the plus direction.

12. A person who shows, say, phobic reactions at hi-plus EMF and who is also suffering from a severe head cold, before getting better may have further phobic manifestations because hi-plus EMF is associated both with physical improvement and also with psychiatric perturbations.

13. Insomnia may also accompany the start of recovery from illness, for nocturnal restlessness is usually associated with hi-plus EMF, particularly in the late night and early morning hours. Similarly, other symptoms, such as migraine, may appear in those so predisposed.

14. In febrile disorders, exaggerated diurnal field shifts correspond with the characteristic body temperature cycle. The patient's temperature tends to be lowest in the early morning hours (usually in the plus direction of the field) and highest in the late afternoon and early evening hours (usually in the minus direction of the field).

15. Unusually vivid dreams tend to be associated with hi-plus intensifications. These show the usual rhythmic variations and often appear just before—and during recovery from—illness.

16. As polarity shows characteristic minus shifts with aging and as these are often associated with the protracted disorders of the elderly, this directing force is in sharp contrast with the strong and unstable energy of youth. Adolescent males tend to show field intensifications of plus polarity and considerable variability.

17. Disorders usually associated with aging, together with behavior disturbances in any age group, seem particularly susceptible to electrocyclic variability.

18. Field phenomena may be significant in the genesis of disorders without known organic cause, especially those which favor regions not circumscribed by specific nerve innervations. Also, despite crude morphologic classifications, electrodynamic field considerations now render the terms "functional psychosis" and "functional disorder" meaningless.

Similarly, various sensory and motor changes effected in hypnotic states as well as in certain behavior disorders can be explained by field changes which can bypass both the central and peripheral nervous systems.

19. Behavior disorders have been measured continuously from *states of excitation* to *states of exhaustion*. In *states of excitation*, clinical improvement is preceded by field detensifications of greater stability. In schizophrenic *states of exhaustion*, clinical improvement is preceded by exaggerated field intensifications usually highly variable, short-lived and rarely noted.

20. Man's senses are often inadequate for direct inspection. Inspection of a car battery, for instance, does not reveal its state of charge, and it is necessary to use a voltmeter. Similarly, man's senses must be amplified by instruments to ascertain the changing states in living systems. This is particularly important in assessing so-called schizophrenic states which span a wide range of voltages from *states of excitation* to *states of exhaustion*.

21. So-called schizophrenic states may reflect incompletely evolved organisms. In cases where the patient displays otherwise superior intelligence, his evolution may be regarded as having been lopsided.

22. All behavior disorders not conditioned by culturally false

conceptions of "normal" reflect, by this construct, an imbalance in the harmonious integration of the old emotional brain core and the newer neocortex. The Burr-Northrop *Theory* makes it possible not only to measure the differences between individuals but also the changes within individuals in time.

23. Aside from so-called natural sciences and theories of neuro-cybernetic information, the Burr-Northrop *Theory* is the first in the behavior field to satisfy Margenau's three principal "metaphysical requirements" for any fertile scientific theory: (1) *simplicity*, (2) *extensibility* and (3) *causality.*

24. Thus, mathematically predicted curves of tree voltages are almost identical to those actually measured. This is only one example of how the Burr-Northrop *Theory* makes it possible to predict by mathematics and the laws of field physics certain consequences in the realms of biology, medicine and behavior.

This, of course, is light years ahead of the theories of many behavior schools, which are the product of archaic philosophies mired in false principles.

25. As with every tradition-shattering discovery, the *Theory* provides some foundation pilings for a bridge between confirmed scientific laws and enlightened values.

26. Electrodynamic man is a complex, highly individuated, meticulously designed, sentient, potentially-thinking electromagnetic system. He has been created by—and responds to—invariant laws which control his rhythmic roller coaster of sequential self-unfolding states.

27. We can now scrap the traditional, complex, pluralistic, specious, Cartesian mind-body theories. We can reject such ghostly Freudian concepts as mental parts and mental forces. We can ignore attempts to reconcile these theories with such psychosomatic concepts of man as a poolroom full of self-sufficient, feelingless, bil-

liard ball-like particles rattling at random through holes in some mythical Swiss cheese.

28. In short, we can abandon the age-old mind-body problem for as Northrop succinctly stated:

> "...there [is] 'no body-mind problem' to solve in the first place, or disembodied ghostly minds, or feelingless and thoughtless human persons, either."

29. The tidal flow and ebb of natural energy have been substantiated in which the continuous flux of intensity and direction have been epistemically correlated with numerous statefunction changes. Thus, an objective measure of those properties of protoplasmic organization which establish the essential characteristics of feeling, behavior and thinking is here, based on non-100% deterministic, mechanical causality principles.

4

Thus, through amplifying his dimly sensed perceptions, man has begun to see shadowy outlines of his celestial roller coaster: following some of the fuzzy borders of the tracks as he is transported in an orderly progression, plotting in space-time its rises and dips at varying positions and momentums, accelerations and decelerations and learning to predict exaggerated, recurrent turns and twists. As a result, he can now begin to appreciate for the first time that, far from being alone, he is in the company of every living thing: each affecting the other, each showing its own individuated response to the general pattern laid down by universal law.

To quote F. L Kunz, former editor of *Main Currents in Modern Thought:*

> "The moment is propitious; we may be close upon the kind of breakthrough in biologic science which has brought the physical sciences to their present degree of control and

refinement. If so, the implications for education, and indeed for all socio-cultural aspects of human life, are without precedent."

References

American Society of Clinical Hypnosis. Oct 3-4,1958. Program, First Annual Meeting, pp. 3.4.

American Society of Clinical Hypnosis. Oct 9-11,1959. Program, Annual Scientific Assembly, pp. 6, 15.

American Society of Clinical Hypnosis. Nov. 15, 1959 Newsletter, p.3; March 3, 1960 Newsletter, p.2.

Anderson, J. D. 1951. Galvanotaxis of slime mold. *J. Gen. Physiol.* 35:1-16.

Anhenius, S. 1898. Die einwirkung kosmïscher einflüsse auf physiologische vërbältnisse. *Skand Arch. Physiol.* 8: 367-416 & 5 plates ff.

Backus, P. S. 1962. The use of hypnotically induced seizures to replace electroshock treatments. *Am. J. Clin. Hyp.* 4: 272-273.

Bagchi, B. K., R. W. Howell & H. T. Schmale. 1945. The electoencephalographic and clinical effects of electrically induced convulsions in the treatment of mental disorders. *Am. J. Psychiat.* 102: 49-61.

Bartlett, K. A. Jr. 1982. *Utilization of Human Electro-Dynamic Fields to Study Hypnosis and Other Altered States of Consciousness (with Suggestions for Further Applications). J. Am. Soc. Psychosom. Dent. Med. Supplement*, No. 3.

Barton, D. S. 1940. Electric correlates of the menstrual cycle in women. *Yale J. Biol. Med.* 12: 503-523.

Becker, R. O. 1961. The bioelectric factors in amphibian-limb regeneration. *J. Bone Joint Surg.* 43A: 643-656.

Becker, R. O. 1961. Electromagnetic mental ills. MD. 5:96.

Becker, R. O. 1961. Electricity and mental illness. *Modern Medicine.* Newsfront. 29: 20.

Bertholon, M. 1783. *De l'Électricité des Végétaux.* (Avec approbation & privilege du Roi). Paris, France: P. F. Didot Jeune.

Blagg, J. Personal communications, unpublished data.

Bliss, C. I. 1958 Periodic regression in biology and climatology. *Bulletin of the Connecticut Agricultural Experiment Station.* 615: 19-21. New Haven, CT.

Borghi, J. H. May 20, 1960. Further feeling-state studies: Application of The P-technic. In Symposium IV: *History of Certain Psychotherapeutic & Forensic Aspects the of Study of Man.* Williamsburg and Ft. Monroe: Eastern State Hospital, College William and Mary and Virginia Society of Clinical Hypnosis. Roof Garden Terrace, The Chamberlin, Fenwick Rd. (US 258), Old Point Comfort, Ft. Monroe.

Brenten, J. H. 1861. Special characteristics of Lawrence Tremlett. v.1: Mad or not mad? In *The Tragedy of Life: Being Records of Remarkable Phases of Lunacy, Kept by a Physician.* London: Smith, Elder and Co., esp. p.191 footnote.

Brown, F. A. Jr. 1962. Extrinsic rhythmicity: a reference frame for biological rhythms under so-called constant conditions. In *Rhythmic Functions in the Living System.* W. Wolf, conference chm. & ed. *An. NY Acad. Sc.* 98 (4): 775-787.

Brown, F. A. Jr. 1976. On the pacemaker for circadian rhythms. In *Theoretical Issues in Biological Rhythm Research.* J. Morgan Thomas, ed. *et al.* 4: 20-27.

Brown, F. A. Jr., M. F. Bennett & W. J. Brett, 1959. Effects of imposed magnetic fields in modifying snail orientation. *Biol. Bul.* 117: 406.

Burr, H. S. 1924. Some experiments on the transplantation of the olfactory placode in Amblystoma. I. An experimentally produced aberrant cranial nerve. *J. Comp. Neur.* 37: 455-479.

Burr, H. S. 1930. Disciplines. *Yale J. Biol. Med.* 3: 151-157.

Burr, H. S. 1932. Ch. 3. Determinants of organization in the cerebral hemispheres. *Proc. Assn. Res. Nerv. Ment. Dis.* 13: 39-18. Baltimore: Williams & Wilkins Co.

Burr, H. S. 1932. An electro-dynamic theory of development suggested by studies of proliferation rates in the brain of Amblystoma. *J. Comp. Neur.* 56: 347-371.

Burr, H. S. 1936. Electro-dynamic studies of mice with developing cancer of the mammary gland. *Anat. Rec.* 64: 7-8.

Burr, H. S. 1937. Bio-electric correlates of development in Amblystoma. *Yale J. Biol. Med.* 9: 541-549.

Burr, H. S. 1939. Animal electricity. *Yale Scientific Mag.* 13: 5.

Burr, H. S. 1940. Biological organization and the cancer problem. *Yale J. Biol. Med.* 12: 277-282.

Burr, H. S. 1941. Changes in the field properties of mice with transplanted tumors. *Yale J. Biol. Med.* 13: 783-788.

Burr, H. S. 1941. Field properties of the developing frog's egg. *Proc. Nat. Acad. Sc. U.S.* 27: 276-281.

Burr, H. S. 1942. Electrical correlates of growth in corn roots. *Yale J. Biol. Med.* 14: 561-565.

Burr, H. S. 1943. An electrometric study of mimosa. *Yale J. Biol. Med.* 15: 823-829.

Burr, H. S. 1943. Electrical correlates of pure and hybrid strains of sweet corn. *Proc. Nat. Acad. Sc. U.S.* 29: 163-166.

Burr, H. S. 1944. Potential gradients in living systems and their measurement. *In Medical Physics*. v. 1: 1117-1121. O. Glasser, ed. Chicago: Year Book Publishers.

Burr, H. S. 1944. Moon-madness. *Yale J. Biol. Med.* 16:249-256.

Burr, H. S. 1944. The meaning of bio-electric potentials. *Yale J. Biol. Med.* 16: 353-360.

Burr, H. S. 1944. Electricity and life: phases of moon correlated with life cycle. *Yale Scientific Mag.* 18: 5-6, 16, 18.

Burr, H. S. 1945. Variables in DC measurement. *Yale J. Biol. Med.* 17: 465-478.

Burr, H. S. 1945. Diurnal potentials in the maple tree. *Yale J. Biol. Med.* 17: 727-734.

Burr, H. S. 1947. Tree potentials. *Yale J. Biol. Med.* 19: 311-318.

Burr, H. S. 1950. Bioelectricity: potential gradients. *In Medical Physics*. v.2: 90-94. O. Glasser, ed. Chicago: Year Book Publishers.

Burr, H. S. 1950. An electrometric study of cotton seeds. *J. Exp. Zool.* 113: 201-210.

Burr, H. S. 1950. Electrocyclic phenomena: recording life dynamics of oak trees. *Yale Scientific Mag.* 25: 9-10, 32, 34, 36, 38, 40.

Burr, H. S. 1952. Electrometrics of atypical growth. *Yale J. Biol. Med.* 25: 67-75.

Burr, H. S. 1954. Confusion or configuration? *Astr. League Bul.* 4: 1-2, 5-8.

Burr, H. S. 1955. Certain electrical properties of the slime mold. *J. Exp. Zool.* 129: 327-342.

Burr, H. S. 1956. Effect of a severe storm on electric properties of a tree and the earth. *Science.* 124: 1204-1205.

Burr, H. S. Nov. 20, 1959. Field Theory in Biology I: Natural history background. Film I: Field correlates of the salamander embryo. In Symposium II: *Field Theory as an Integrator of Knowledge.* Williamsburg: Eastern State Hospital, College of William and Mary and Virginia Society of Clinical Hypnosis. Washington 100, W & M.

Burr, H. S. Nov. 21, 1959. Field Theory in Biology II: Experimental findings of the logical consequences of field theory in biology. In Symposium II: *Field Theory as an Integrator of Knowledge.* Williamsburg: Eastern State Hospital, College of William and Mary and Virginia Society of Clinical Hypnosis. Dodge Room, Phi Beta Kappa Memorial Hall, W & M.

Burr, H. S. 1960. A basis for a theory of law: Natural law as the source of universals for society and for the individual. *Main Currents in Modern Thought.* 17: 3-7.

Burr, H. S. 1960. Bioelectricity: measurement of electrodynamic fields. In *Medical Physics.* v. 3: 59-61. O. Glasser, ed. Chicago: Year Book Publishers.

Burr, H. S. 1960. *The Neural Basis of Human Behavior.* Springfield: Charles C. Thomas, Publisher.

Burr, H. S. 1962. *The Nature of Man and the Meaning of Existence.* Springfield: Charles C. Thomas, Publisher.

Burr, H. S. Sep.-Oct 1962. Some results of *electro-dynamic theory:* A report by one of the authors of The Electro-Dynamic Theory of some of the experimental studies which are demonstrating the applicability of the Theory to problems of growth and biological organization. *Main Currents in Modern Thought.* Special issue commemorating the Burr-Northrop *Electro-Dynamic Theory of Life.* 19: 11-12.

Burr, H. S. 1972, 1977, 1982, 1988. *Blueprint for Immortality: The Electric Patterns of Life.* London & Sudbury, Suffolk: Neville Spearman, bought by The C. W. Daniel Co. Ltd., 1 Church Path,

Saffron Walden, Essex CB10 1JP, England. N. Am. edn., 1973. *The Fields of Life: Our Links with the Universe.* New York & Toronto: Ballantine.

For other pertinent Burr references, 1916-1956, and the Boris Artzybasheff portrait of Burr presented to Yale Medical School, see Davenport Hooker's article, initialed D. H., commemorating his Yale retirement, 1957. *Yale J. Biol. Med.* 30: 161-167; and Appendix, Bibliography of Harold Saxton Burr, in *Blueprint for Immorality: The Electric Patterns of Life.* London & Sudbury, Suffolk: Neville Spearman, bought by The C. W. Daniel Co. Ltd., 1 Church Path, Saffron Walden, Essex CB10 1JP, England, pp. 185-192. N. Am. edn., 1973. *The Fields of Life: Our Links with the Universe.* New York, & Toronto: Ballantine, pp. 207-215.

Burr, H. S. 1947-1973. Personal communications and letters.

Burr, H. S. & D. S. Barton. 1938. Steady-state electrical properties of the human organism during sleep. *Yale J. Biol. Med.* 10: 271-274.

Burr, H. S. & J. Boling. 1941. Factors associated with vaginal electrical correlates of the estrous cycle of the albino rat. *Anat. Rec.* 79: 9.

Burr, H. S. & T. H. Bullock. 1941. Steady state potential differences in the early development of Amblystoma. *Yale J. Biol. Med.* 14: 51-57.

Burr, H. S. & T. H. Bullock. 1943. Electrical polarization of pacemaker neurons. *J. Neurophysiol.* 6: 85-97.

Burr, H. S. & V. L. Gott. 1953. Electrical correlates of ovulation in the rhesus monkey. *Yale J. Biol. Med.* 25: 408-417

Burr, H. S. & F. S. Hammett. 1939. A preliminary study of electrical correlates of growth in Obelia geniculata. *Growth.* 3: 211-220.

Burr, H. S. & P. J. Harman Jr. 1939. Voltage gradients in the nervous system. *Tr. Am. Neur. Assn.* 65: 11-14.

Burr, H. S., S. C. Harvey & M. Taffel. 1938. Bio-electric correlates of wound healing. *Yale J. Biol. Med.* 11: 103-107.

Burr, H. S., R. T. Hill & E. Allen. 1935. Detection of ovulation in the intact rabbit. *Proc. Soc. Exp. Biol. Med.* 33: 109-111.

Burr, H. S. & C. I. Hovland, 1937. Bio-electric potential gradients in the chick. *Yale J. Biol. Med.* 9: 247-258.

Burr, H. S. & C. I. Hovland, 1937. Bio-electric correlates of development in Amblystoma. *Yale J. Biol. Med.* 9: 546-549.

Burr, H. S. & C. T. Lane. 1935. Electrical characteristics of living systems. *Yale J. Biol. Med.* 8: 31-35.

Burr, H. S., C. T. Lane & L. F. Nims. 1936. A vacuum tube micro-voltmeter for the measurement of bio-electric phenomena. *Yale J. Biol. Med.* 9: 65-76.

Burr, H. S. & R. B. Livingston, 1952. Effect of hypoxia and hypercapnea on standing potential of man. *Federation Proc.* 11: 21.

Burr. H. S. & A. Mauro. 1949. Millivoltmeters. *Yale J. Biol. Med.* 21: 249-253.

Burr, H. S. & A. Mauro. 1949. Electrostatic fields of the sciatic nerve in the frog. *Yale J. Biol. Med.* 21: 455-462.

Burr, H. S. & L. K. Musselman. 1936. Bio-electric phenomena associated with menstruation. *Yale J. Biol. Med.* 9: 155-158.

Burr, H. S. & L. K. Musselman. 1938. Bio-electric correlates of the menstrual cycle in women. *Am. J. Ob. Gyn.* 35: 743-751.

Burr, H. S., L. K. Musselman, D. S. Barton & N B. Kelly. 1937. A bio-electric record of human ovulation. *Science.* 86: 312.

Burr, H. S., L. K. Musselman, D. S. Barton & N .B. Kelly. 1937. Bio-electric correlates of human ovulation. *Yale J. Biol. Med.* 10: 155-160.

Burr, H. S. & O. E. Nelson Jr. 1946. Growth correlates of electro-motive force in maize seeds. *Proc. Nat. Acad. Sc. U.S.* 32: 73-84.

Burr, H. S. & F. S. C. Northrop. 1935. The Electro-Dynamic Theory of Life. *Q. Rev. Biol.* 10: 322-333. Reprinted Sep./Oct. 1962 in *Main Currents in Modern Thought*. Special issue commemorating the Burr-Northrop Theory. 19: 4-10.

Burr, H. S. & F. S. C. Northrop. 1937. Experimental findings concerning the Electro-Dynamic Theory of Life and an analysis of their physical meaning. *Growth.* 1: 78-88.

Burr, H. S. & F. S. C. Northrop. 1939. Evidence for the existence of an electro-dynamic field in living organisms. *Proc. Nat. Acad. Sc. U.S.* 25: 284-288.

Burr, H. S. & W. Seifriz 1955. Response of the slime mold to electric stimulus. *Science.* 122: 1020-1021.

Burr, H. S. & E. W. Sinnott. 1944. Electrical correlates of form in cucurbit fruits. *Am. J. Botany.* 21: 249-253.

Burr, H. S., G. M. Smith & L. C. Strong. 1938. Bioelectric properties of cancer-resistant and cancer-susceptible mice. *Am. J. Cancer.* 32: 240-248.

Burr, H. S., G. M. Smith & L. C. Strong. 1940. Electrometric studies of tumors in mice induced by the external application of benzpyrene. *Yale J. Biol. Med.* 12: 711-717.

Burr, H. S. & P. K. Smith. 1938. The relationship between the bioelectric potential of rats and certain drugs. *Yale J. Biol. Med.* 11: 137-140.

Burr, H. S., L. C. Strong & G .M. Smith. 1938. Bio-electric correlates of methyl colanthrene-induced tumors in mice. *Yale J. Biol. Med.* 10: 539-544.

Burr, H. S., M. Taffel & S. C. Harvey, 1940. An electrometric study of the healing wound in man. *Yale J. Biol. Med.* 12: 483-485.

Churchill, D. A. 1964. A variation of the "as-if-EST" hypnotic technique: a clinical note. *Am. J. Clin. Hyp.* 7: 172-173.

Coghill, G. E. 1916. Correlated anatomical and physiological studies on the growth of the nervous system of Amphibia, II. The afferent system on the head of Amblystoma. *J. Comp. Neur.* 26: 247-340.

Cooper, L. F. & M. H. Erickson. 1950. Time distortion in hypnosis, II. *Bul. Georgetown U. Med. Ctr.* 2: 50-68. Reprinted 1952 in *Experimental Hypnosis*. L. M. LeCron, ed. New York: Macmillan, pp. 222-240.

Cooper, L. F. & M. H. Erickson. 1954, 1959. *Time Distortion in Hypnosis: An Experimental and Clinical Investigation*. Baltimore: Williams & Wilkins.

Cuadra, C. A. 1954. An experimental evaluation of the relaxation-persuasion technique for the treatment of chronic schizophrenia. Downey Veterans Administration Hospital, N. Chicago (mimeographed).

Cuadra, C. A. 1956. Final report on the rehabilitation research project. Downey Veterans Administration Hospital, N. Chicago (mimeographed).

Davis, J. E. 1957. *Recovery from Schizophrenia: The Roland Method.* Springfield: Charles C Thomas, Publisher.

Davis, P. A. 1941. Technique and evaluation of the electroencephalogram. *J. Neurophysiol*. 4: 92-114.

Derbyshire, A. J. & L. J. Ravitz. 1958. An adjuvant to electroencephalographic analyses, with accompanying EEG classification chart. *Neuropsychiatry*. 4: 189-192. Charlottesville: U. VA. Medical School. Part of EEG classification chart reprinted in Schwab, R. S. 1951. *Electroencephalography in Clinical Practice*. Philadelphia: W. B. Saunders, p. 31.

De Tata, J. C., L. R. Roddy & L. J. Ravitz. May 20, 1960. Observations on certain trance phenomena: Improved motor skills in driving. Heightened perceptions and discriminations pertaining to illegal acts. In Symposium IV: *History of Certain Psychotherapeutic & Forensic Aspects of the Study of Man.* Williamsburg and Ft. Monroe: Eastern State Hospital, College of William and Mary and Virginia Society of Clinical Hypnosis. Roof Garden Terrace, The Chamberlin, Fenwick Rd. (US 258) Old Point Comfort, Ft. Monroe.

DuBois-Reymond, E. 1848, 1849 & 1860. *Untersuchungen über thierische Elektricität* Berlin: G. Reimer.

Einstein, A. 1950. *The Meaning of Relativity* (incl. The Generalized Theory of Gravitation). 3d edn. Princeton: Princeton University Press.

Einstein, A. 1949. Reply. In *Albert Einstein: Philosopher-Scientist.* P. A. Schilpp, ed. La Salle: Open Court, & London: Cambridge University Press, pp. 683-684.

Ekholm, N. & S. Arrhenius. 1894-1895. Bihang till Sv. Vetensk. *Akad. Handl.* Bd. XIX, afd I. nr. 8 & bd. XX, afd. I, nr. 6, Stockholm, Sweden.

Ekholm, N. & S. Arrhenius. 1898. *Ibid.* Bd. XXXI, nr. 2.

Ekholm, N. & S. Arrhenius. 1898. *Ibid.* Bd. XXXI, nr. 3.

Electricity and life: currents in plants and animals link them to universe. Aug. 14, 1944, *Life.* 17 #7: 85-86, 89.

Ellis, H. 1900. The phenomena of sexual periodicity. 1: 49-109. Sexual periodicity in men by F. H. Perry-Coste. 1: 218-230, charts I-XIII. 1: 255-276; 1928. The menstrual cycle of sexual impulse. 7: 213-236. In Havelock Ellis, *Studies in the Psychology of Sex.* Philadelphia: F. A. Davis.

Erickson, M. H. 1932. Possible detrimental effects from experimental hypnosis. *J. Abn. Soc. Psychol.* 27: 321-327.

Erickson, M. H. 1933. The investigation of a specific amnesia. *Brit. J. Med. Psychol.* 13: 143-150.

Erickson, M. H. 1935. A study of an experimental neurosis hypnotically induced in a case of ejaculatio praecox. *Brit. J. Med. Psychol.* 15: 34-50.

Erickson, M. H. 1937. An experimental demonstration of unconscious mentation by automatic writing. *Psychoanal. Quart.* 6: 513-529.

Erickson, M. H. 1937. Development of apparent unconsciousness during hypnotic reliving of a traumatic experience. *Arch. Neur. Psychiat.* 38: 1282-1288.

Erickson, M. H. 1938. The problem of the definition and the dynamic values of psychiatric concepts. Part I. General considerations. M. Rec. 148: 107-109. Part II. Case history. *Ibid.* 148: 185-189.

Erickson, M. H. 1938. A study of clinical and experimental findings on hypnotic deafness: I. Clinical experimentation and findings. *J. Gen. Psychol.* 19: 127-150.

Erickson, M. H. 1938. A study of clinical and experimental findings on hypnotic deafness: II. Experimental findings with a conditioned response technique. *J. Gen. Psychol.* 19: 151-167.

Erickson, M. H. 1939. The induction of color blindness by a technique of hypnotic suggestion. *J. Gen. Psychol.* 20: 61-89.

Erickson, M. H. 1939. The application of hypnosis to psychiatry. *Med. Rec.* 150: 60-65.

Erickson, M. H. 1939. Experimental demonstrations of the psychopathology of everyday life. *Psychoanal. Quart.* 8: 338-353.

Erickson, M. H. 1939. An experimental investigation of the possible antisocial use of hypnosis. *Psychiat.* 2: 391-414.

Erickson, M. H. 1939. Demonstration of mental mechanisms by hypnosis. *Arch. Neur. Psychiat.* 42: 367-370.

Erickson, M. H. 1940. The appearance in three generations of an atypical pattern of the sneezing reflex. *J. Genetic Psychol.* 56: 455-459.

Erickson, M. H. 1941. Hypnosis: a general review. *Dis. Nerv. System.* 2: 13-18.

Erickson, M. H. 1941. The early recognition of mental disease. *Dis. Nerv. System.* 2: 99-108.

Erickson, M H. 1941. On the possible occurrence of a dream in an eight-month-old infant. *Psychoanal. Quart.* 10: 382-384.

Erickson, M. H. 1943. Hypnotic investigation of psychosomatic phenomena: psychosomatic interrelationships studied by experimental hypnosis. *Psychosom. Med.* 5: 51-58.

Erickson, M. H. 1943. A controlled experimental use of hypnotic regression in the therapy of an acquired food intolerance. *Psychosom. Med.* 5: 67-70.

Erickson, M. H. 1943. Experimentally elicited salivary and related responses to hypnotic visual hallucinations confirmed by personality reactions. *Psychosom. Med.* 5: 185-187.

Erickson, M. H. 1944. A teaching program for commissioned reserve officers. *Dis. Nerv. System.* 5: 112-115.

Erickson, M. H. 1944. The method employed to formulate a complex story for the induction of an experimental neurosis in a hypnotic subject. *J. Gen. Psychol.* 31: 67-84.

Erickson, M. H. 1944. An experimental investigation of the hypnotic subject's apparent ability to become unaware of stimuli. *J. Gen. Psychol.* 31: 191-212.

Erickson, M. H. 1944. Hypnosis in medicine. In *Medical Clinics of North America. New York Number*. Philadelphia: W. B. Saunders Co., pp. 639-652.

Erickson, M. H. 1945. Hypnotic techniques for the therapy of acute psychiatric disturbances in war. *Am. J. Psychiat*. 101: 668-672.

Erickson, M. H. 1952. Deep hypnosis and its induction. In *Experimental Hypnosis*. L. M. LeCron, ed. New York: Macmillan, pp. 70-114.

Erickson, M. H. 1952-1962. Hypnosis or hypnotism. *Collier's Encyclopedia,* 1st edn. New York: Crowell-Collier.

Erickson, M. H. 1953. The therapy of a psychosomatic headache. *J. Clin. Exp. Hyp*. 1: 2-6.

Erickson, M. H. 1954-1960. Hypnotism. *Encyclopaedia Britannica,* 14th edn. 1961-1973. Hypnosis. *Encyclopaedia Britannica,* 14th edn.

Erickson, M. H. 1954. The development of an acute limited obsessional hysterical state in a normal hypnotic subject. *J. Clin. Exp. Hyp*. 2: 27-41.

Erickson, M. H. 1954. Special techniques of brief hypnotherapy. *J. Clin. Exp. Hyp*. 2: 109-129.

Erickson, M. H. 1954. A clinical note on indirect hypnotic therapy. *J. Clin. Exp. Hyp*. 2: 171-174.

Erickson, M. H. 1954. Pseudo-orientation in time as a hypnotherapeutic procedure. *J. Clin. Exp. Hyp*. 2: 261-283.

Erickson, M. H. 1955. Self-exploration in the hypnotic state. *J. Clin. Exp. Hyp*. 3: 49-57.

Erickson, M. H. 1955. The hypnotherapy of two psychosomatic dental problems. *J. Am. Soc. Psychosom. Dent*. 1: 6-10.

Erickson, M. H. 1958. Naturalistic techniques of hypnosis. *Am. J. Clin. Hyp*. 1: 3-8.

Erickson, M. H. 1959. Hypnosis in painful terminal illness. *Am. J. Clin. Hyp*. 2: 117-121.

Erickson, M. H. 1959. Further clinical techniques of hypnosis:

utilization techniques. *Am. J. Clin. Hyp.* 2: 3-21.

Erickson, M. H. April 23, 1959. Uses of hypnosis. In Symposium I: *Hypnosis in Psychiatry and Medicine.* Ft. Monroe: Eastern State Hospital and Virginia Society of Clinical Hypnosis. The Chamberlin, Fenwick Rd. (US 258), Old Point Comfort.

Erickson, M. H. Dec. 9, 1959. Experiential factors in symptom formation. "Psychosomatic" interrelationships and interdependencies. In Symposium III: *Hypnosis in Office Practice.* Williamsburg: Eastern State Hospital, Williamsburg-James City County Medical Society and Virginia Society of Clinical Hypnosis. Dunbar 43 Room l, Rt 615, ESH.

Erickson, M. H. Dec. 10, 1959. Symptomatology. In Symposium III: *Hypnosis in Office Practice.* Williamsburg: Eastern State Hospital, Williamsburg-James City County Medical Society and Virginia Society of Clinical Hypnosis. Administration Bldg., Room 130, Rt 322, ESH.

Erickson, M. H. Dec. 10, 1959. "Schizophrenia." In Symposium III: *Hypnosis in Office Practice.* Williamsburg: Eastern State Hospital, Williamsburg-James City County Medical Society and Virginia Society of Clinical Hypnosis. Dunbar 43, Room 1, Rt 615, ESH.

Erickson, M. H. Dec. 10, 1959. Advanced understanding and techniques. Time distortion in space travel. In Symposium III: *Hypnosis in Office Practice.* Williamsburg: Eastern State Hospital, Williamsburg-James City County Medical Society and Virginia Society of Clinical Hypnosis. Dining Room, Motor House Cafeteria.

Erickson, M. H. 1960. Breast development possibly influenced by hypnosis: two instances and the psychotherapeutic results. *Am. J. Clin. Hyp.* 2: 157-159.

Erickson, M. H. 1960. Psychogenic alteration of menstrual functioning: three instances. *Am. J. Clin. Hyp.* 2: 227-231.

Erickson, M. H. 1961. Historical note on the hand levitation and other ideomotor techniques. *Am. J. Clin. Hyp.* 3: 196-199. Spanish translation 1961, in *Revista Latino-Americana de Hipnosis Clinica.* Ciertos principios en la hipnosis medica. 2: 67-69.

Erickson, M. H. 1961. An instance of potentially harmful misinterpretation of hypnosis. *Am. J. Clin. Hyp.* 3: 242-243.

Erickson, M. H. 1962. An investigation of optokinetic nystagmus. *Am. J. Clin. Hyp.* 4: 181-188.

Erickson, M. H. 1962. Basic psychological problems in hypnotic research. In *Hypnosis: Current Problems.* G. Estabrooks, ed. New York: Harper and Row, pp. 207-223.

Erickson, M. H. 1963. An application of implications of Lashley's researches in a circumscribed arteriosclerotic brain condition. *Perceptual and Motor Skills.* 16: 779-780.

Erickson, M. H. 1963. Chemo-anesthesia in relation to hearing and memory. *Am. J. Clin. Hyp.* 6: 31-36.

Erickson, M. H. 1963. Hypnotically oriented psychotherapy in organic brain damage. *Am. J. Clin. Hyp.* 6: 92-112.

Erickson, M. H. 1964. The confusion technique in hypnosis. *Am. J. Clin. Hyp.* 6: 183-207.

Erickson, M.H. 1964. The "surprise" and "my-friend-John" techniques of hypnosis: minimal cues and natural field experimentation. *Am. J. Clin. Hyp.* 6: 293-307.

Erickson, M. H. 1964. An hypnotic technique for resistant patients: the patient, the technique and its rationale, and field experiments. *Am. J. Clin. Hyp.* 7: 8-32.

Erickson, M. H. 1964. Pantomime techniques in hypnosis and the implications. *Am. J. Clin. Hyp.* 7: 64-70.

Erickson, M. H. 1964. Initial experiments investigating the

nature of hypnosis. *Am. J. Clin. Hyp.* 7: 152-162.

Erickson, M. H. 1965. Acquired control of pupillary responses. *Am. J. Clin. Hyp.* 7: 207-208.

Erickson, M. H. 1965. A special inquiry with Aldous Huxley into the nature and character of various states of consciousness. *Am. J. Clin. Hyp.* 8: 14-33.

Erickson, M. H. 1967. *Advanced Techniques of Hypnosis and Therapy: Selected Papers of Milton H. Erickson, M.D.* Jay Haley, ed. New York & London: Grune & Stratton, Publishers. Partial bibliography to 1967, pp. 523-529.

Erickson, M. H. 1967. Laboratory and clinical hypnosis: the same or different phenomena? *Am. J. Clin. Hyp.* 9: 166-170.

Erickson, M. H. 1967. Further experimental investigation of hypnosis: hypnotic and nonhypnotic realities. *Am. J. Clin. Hyp.* 10: 87-135.

Erickson, M. H. 1967. Hypnosis: its renascence as a treatment modality. *Trends in Psychiat.* 3: 3-43.

Erickson, M. H. 1980. *The Collected Papers of Milton H. Erickson on Hypnosis.* E. L. Rossi, ed. 4 vols. New York: Irvington Publishers.

Erickson, M. H. 1945-1980. Personal communications and letters, esp. Thanksgiving conferences, Nov. 21-24, 1972 & Nov. 22-23, 1979, Phoenix.

Erickson, M. H. & Brickner, R. M. 1943. The development of aphasia-like reactions from hypnotically induced amnesias. Experimental observations and a detailed case report. *Psychosom. Med.* 5: 59-66.

Erickson, M. H. & E. M. Erickson. 1938. The hypnotic induction of hallucinatory color vision followed by pseudo-negative afterimages. *J. Exp. Psychol.* 22: 581-588.

Erickson, M. H. & E. M. Erickson. 1941. Concerning the nature and character of posthypnotic behavior. *J. Gen. Psychol.* 24: 95-133.

Erickson, M. H. & E. M. Erickson. 1958. Further considerations of time distortion: Subjective time condensation as distinct from time expansion, *Am. J. Clin. Hyp.* 1: 83-88.

Erickson, M. H., S. Hershman & I. I. Secter. 1961. *The Practical Application of Medical and Dental Hypnosis.* New York: The Julian Press, Inc.

Erickson, M. H. & L. S. Kubie. 1938. The use of automatic drawing in the interpretation and relief of a state of acute obsessional depression. *Psychoanal. Quart.* 7: 443-466.

Erickson, M. H. & L. S. Kubie. 1939. The permanent relief of an obsessional phobia by means of communication with an unsuspected dual personality. *Psychoanal. Quart.* 8: 471-509.

Erickson, M. H. & L. S. Kubie. 1941. The successful treatment of a case of acute hysterical depression by return under hypnosis to a critical phase of childhood. *Psychoanal. Quart.* 10: 593-609.

Erickson, M. H. & E. L. Rossi. 1979. *Hypnotherapy, An Exploratory Case Book.* New York: Irvington Publishers.

Erickson, M. H., E. L. Rossi & S. I. Rossi. 1979. *Hypnotic Realities.* New York: Irvington Publishers.

Erickson, M. H. & E. L. Rossi. 1981. *Experiencing Hypnosis: Therapeutic Approaches to Altered States.* New York: Irvington Publishers.

For other pertinent Erickson writings not referenced here and in *Advanced Techniques of Hypnosis and Therapy*, 1967, p. 217 of this bibliography, can be found in Gravitz, M. A. & R. F. Gravitz, 1977. The collected writings of Milton H. Erickson, a complete bibliography 1929-1977. *Am. J. Clin. Hyp.* commemorative edn, 20: 84-94.

Faraday, M. 1839. Read 1833. Animal electricity. In his *Experimental Researches in Electricity.* V. 1 99-102, pars. 351-360.

London: Bernard Quaritch.

Faraday, M. 1844. Read 1838. Notice of the character and direction of the electric force of the Gymnotus. In his *Experimental Researches in Electricity*. v. 2: 1-17, pars. 1749-1795. London: Bernard Quaritch.

Field Theory as an Integrator of Knowledge, Symposium II. Nov. 20-21, 1959. Featuring H. S. Burr, Ph.B., Ph.D.; Henry Margenau, B.A., M.S., Ph.D., L.H.D.; F. S. C. Northrop, B.A., M.A., Ph.D., LL.D. & L. J. Ravitz, B.S., M.S., M.D. Williamsburg: Eastern State Hospital, College of William and Mary and Virginia Society of Clinical Hypnosis.

Fonseca, J. S. da, ed., contrib. & others. 1970. *Signification and Intention*. Gulbenkian Fdn. edn., Lisbon, Portugal. Pub. by Clinica Psiquiatrica da Faculdade de Medicina de Lisboa, Laboratorio de Neurofisiologia, Cento de Estudos Egas Moniz, Universidad de Lisboa. Ptd. in English. Reprinted in 1975 with later studies in *If Life...Then One Among at Least Four.* 1: 29-116; 1976, 2: 1-64. Horace G. Oliver Jr., Publisher, 352 Sylvan Ave., Leonia, NJ 07605.

In 1970,[1] a unified tripartite logic for psychology and psychiatry was formalized mathematically and elaborated for its cognative epistemological, pedagogical, linguistic and psychiatrical applications. This logic (a) extends the epistemology and scientific methods of mathematical physical entities to individual persons as suggested in 1939,[2] while also (b) adding an intentional logic for human meaning and intentions. Its three parts are:

(C^1) An irreducible[3] n-adic intentional Calculus of Relations with its relational analytic logic of systems.

(C^2) A relationally analytic Tensorial Calculus.

(C^3) An epistemically correlated[4] Calculus of Matrical Operators.[5]

[1]Fonseca, J. S. da, ed., contrib. & others. *Signification and Intention*, above.

[2]Northrop, F. S. C. Body and mind. For social relations, see Northrop's 1948 The neurological and behavioristic basis of the ordering of society by means of ideas. Both referenced herein.

[3]For the reason why, see Northrop, F. S. C. 1970. The relation between naturalistic scientific knowledge and humanistic intrinsic values in western culture, referenced herein.

[4]Northrop, F. S. C. 1947. Epistemic correlations and operational definitions. See also the equivalent rules of correspondence which evolved into epistemic rules of correspondence. Margenau, H. 1950. *The Nature of Physical Reality: A Philosophy of Modern Physics,* and subsequent papers referenced herein.

[5]Fonseca, J. S. da & F. S. C. Northrop. 1975. Referenced herein.

Fonseca, J. S. da & W. S. McCulloch, 1967. Synthesis and linearization of non-linear feedback shift registers—basis of a model of memory. *Q. Prog. Report No. 86. Research Laboratory of Electronics, M.I.T.* Cambridge, p. 355.

Fonseca, J. S. da & F. S. C. Northrop. 1975. Can Interpersonal Neurophysicological Relations be Rigorously Defined Mathematically and Assessed Experimentally within a Systems Approach as a Human Factor in Psychology and its Psychiatry and in Legal Science and its *due processed* Political Practices? *If Life...Then One Among at Least Four*. 1: 4-8.

Fox, H. M. 1928. *Selene or Sex and the Moon*. Psyche Miniatures General Series No. 15. London: Kegan Paul, Trench, Trubner & Co. Ltd.

Freke, J. 1752. *A Treatise on the Nature and Property of Fire. In Three Essays.* London: W. Innys, and J. Richardson.

Fulton, J. F. & A. D. Keller. 1932. *The Sign of Babinski: A Study of the Evolution of Cortical Dominance in Primates*. Springfield: Charles

C Thomas, Publisher.

Gibbs, J. W. 1928. Thermodynamics. In his *Collected Works.* v. 1: 429. W. R. Longley & R. G. Van Name, eds. New York: Longmans, Green & Co.

Gjessing, R. L. 1938. Disturbances of somatic function in catatonia with a periodic course, and their compensation. *J. Ment. Sc.* 84: 608-621.

Gralnick, A. 1942. *Folie á deux*—the psychosis of association. A review of 103 cases and the entire English literature: with case presentations. *Psychiat. Quart.* 16: 230-263.

Grenell, R. G. & H. S. Burr. 1946. Electrical correlates of peripheral nerve injury: a preliminary note. *Science.* 103: 48-49.

Grenell, R. G. & H. S. Burr. 1946. Surface potentials and peripheral nerve injury: a clinical test. *Yale J. Biol. Med.* 18: 517-525.

Guggenheim, E. A. 1929. The conceptions of electrical potential difference between two phases and the individual activities of ions. *J. Phys. Chem.* 33: 842-849.

Guggenheim, E. A. 1930. On the conception of electrical potential difference between two phases. II. *J. Phys. Chem.* 34: 1540-1543.

Harned, H. S. 1926. Individual thermodynamic behaviors of ions in concentrated solutions including a discussion of the thermodynamic method of computing liquid junction potentials. *J. Phys. Chem.* 30: 433-456.

Herrick, C. J. 1956. *The Evolution of Human Nature.* Austin: University of Texas Press.

Herschel, J. F. W. 1864. *Outlines of Astronomy*, 7th edn. London: Longman, Green, Longman, Roberts, & Green. Introduction, (1.) pp. 1-2; (10a.)-(10b.) pp. 9-10; (417.) p. 273.

Ingvar, S. 1920. Reaction of cells to the galvanic current in tissue cultures. *Proc. Soc. Exp. Biol. Med.* 17: 198-199.

Kallmann, F. J. 1938. *The Genetics of Schizophrenia.* New York: J. J. Augustin.

Kallmann, F. J. 1952. Twin and sibship study of overt male homosexuality. *Am. J. Human Genetics.* 4: 136-146.

Kallmann, F. J. 1953. *Heredity in Health and Mental Disorder.* New York: W. W. Norton & Co.

Kallmann, F. J. & S. E. Barrera. 1942. The heredoconstitutional mechanisms of predisposition and resistance to schizophrenia. *Am. J. Psychiat.* 98: 544-550.

Kallmann, F. J. & J. S. Mickey. 1946. The concept of induced insanity in family units. *J. Nerv. Ment. Dis.* 104: 303-315.

King, C. D. 1945. The meaning of normal. *Yale J. Biol. Med.* 17: 493-501.

King, C. D. 1945. Psychology and the scientific fallacy. *Yale J. Biol. Med.* 18: 541-550.

King, C. D. 1946. Electrometric studies of sleep. *J. Gen. Psychol.* 25: 131-159.

Kunz, F. L. 1962. To the reader. *Main Currents in Modern Thought* 19: 3.

Landahl, H. D., W. S. McCulloch & W. H. Pitts. 1943. A statistical consequence of the logical calculus of nervous nets. *Bul. Math. Biophys.* 51: 135-137.

Langman, L. 1972, 1977, 1982, 1988. The implications of the electro-metric test in cancer of the female genital tract. In H. S. Burr. *Blueprint for Immortality: The Electric Patterns of Life.* London & Sudbury, Suffolk: Neville Spearman, pp. 137-154, bought by The C. W. Daniel Co. Ltd., 1 Church Path, Saffron Walden, Essex CB10 1JP, England. In H. S. Burr. 1973 N. Am. edn. *The Fields of Life: Our Links with the Universe*. New York & Toronto: Ballantine, pp. 151-172.

Langman, L. & H. S. Burr. 1941. An electrometric study of uterine activity. *Am. J. Ob. Gyn*. 42: 59-67.

Langman, L. & H. S. Burr. 1942. An electrical study of the human cervix uteri. *Anat. Rec*. 82: 35-36.

Langman, L. & H. S. Burr. 1942. Electrometric timing of human ovulation. *Am. J. Ob. Gyn*. 44: 223-230.

Langman. L. & H. S. Burr. 1947. Electrometric studies in women with malignancy of cervix uteri. *Science*. 105: 209-210.

Langman, L. & H. S. Burr. 1949. A technique to aid in the detection of malignancy of the female genital tract. *Am. J. Ob. Gyn*. 57: 274-281.

Lardner, D. 1854. *The Museum of Science and Art*, v. 1: 113. London: Walton and Maberly.

Lewis, T. B. Jr. & J. B. Young. 1972. *Christmas in New England*. New York, Chicago & San Francisco: Holt, Rinehart and Winston, p. 9.

Lieber. A. L. 1978. Human aggression and the lunar synodic cycle. *J. Clin. Psychiat*. 39: 385-387, 390-393.

Lund, E. J. 1947. *Bioelectric Fields and Growth* (with a bibliography of continuous bioelectric currents and bioelectric fields in animals and plants by H. F. Rosene). Austin: University of Texas Press.

Lyman, R. S., V. Maeker & P. Liang, eds. & contribs. 1939. *Social and Psychological Studies in Neuropsychiatry in China*. Peking: Published for the Division of Neuropsychiatry, Peking Union Medical College by Henri Vetch.

Lyman, R. S. 1963. *Classics in Neurology Selected by Richard Sherman Lyman, M.D.*, H. S. Burr, ed. Springfield: Charles C Thomas, Publisher.

MacLean, P. D. 1990. *The Triune Brain in Evolution: Role in Paleocerebral Functions.* New York & London: Plenum Press.

Margenau, H. 1947. Particle and field concepts in biology. *Scientific Monthly*. 64: 225-231.

Margenau, H. 1950. *The Nature of Physical Reality: A Philosophy of Modern Physics*, esp. Causality; 19.9 causation in biology: 415. New York: McGraw Hill.

Margenau, H. 1954. Advantages and disadvantages of various interpretations of the quantum theory. *J. Wash. Acad. Sc*. 44: 265-276.

Margenau, H. Nov. 21, 1959. Field theory in physics. In Symposium II: *Field Theory as an Integrator of Knowledge.* Williamsburg: Eastern State Hospital, College of William and Mary and Virginia Society of Clinical Hypnosis. Dodge Room, Phi Beta Kappa Memorial Hall, W & M.

Margenau, H. 1960. Causality: scientific indeterminancy and human freedom—an appraisal. Based upon lecture given at The New School in 1956-1957, cosponsored by the Foundation for Integrated Education. *Main Currents in Modern Thought* 17: 8-13.

Markson, R. 1971. Part I. Considerations regarding solar and lunar modulation of geophysical parameters, atmospheric electricity and thunderstorms. *Pure Apl. Geophys*. 84: 161-202.

Markson, R. 1972, 1977, 1982, 1988. Tree potentials and external factors. In H. S. Burr, *Blueprint for Immortality: The Electric Patters of Life,* London & Sudbury, Suffolk: Neville Spearman, pp. 166-184, bought by The C. W. Daniel Co. Ltd., 1 Church Path, Saffron Walden, Essex CB10 1JP, England. In H. S. Burr. 1973. N. Am. edn. *The Fields of Life: Our Links with the Universe.* New York & Toronto: Ballantine, pp. 186-206.

Markson, R. April 25-26, 1975. The problem in designing a critical experiment when studying geophysical effects on a biological system. In *Proceedings of the Nature and Nurture of Life Conference*. D. D. Harrison, conference director & ed. State University of New York at Stony Brook, pp. 37-70.

Marsh, G. 1930. The effect of applied electric currents on inherent cellular E.M.F. and its possible significance in cell correlation. *Protoplasma*. 11: 447-474.

Marsh, G. & H. W. Beams. 1945. The orientation of pollen tubes of Vinca in the electric current. *J. Cell. Comp. Physiol.* 25: 195-204.

Marsh, G. & H. W. Beams. 1946. In vitro control of chick nerve fibers by applied electric currents. *J. Cell. Comp. Physiol.* 27: 139-157.

Marsh, G. & H. W. Beams. 1952. Electrical control of morphogenesis in regenerating Dugesia tigrina. I. Relation of axial polarity to field strength. *J. Cell. Comp. Physiol.* 39: 191-213.

Mathews, A. P. 1903. Electrical polarity in the hydroids. *Am. J. Physiol.* 8: 294-299.

Maxwell, J. C. 1890. Rec. 27 Oct., read 8 Dec. 1864. A dynamical theory of the electromagnetic field. I. Introductory. In *The Scientific Papers of James Clerk Maxwell.* v. 1: 533, par. (16). Cambridge: Cambridge University Press.

McCulloch, W. S. 1967. Ch. XIV. Lekton, being a belated introduction to the thesis of Eilhard von Domarus. In *Communications: Theory and Research, Proceedings of the First International Symposium*. L. O. Thayer, ed. Springfield: Charles C Thomas, Publisher, pp. 348-350.

McCulloch, W. S. 1967. Ch. XVI. Commentary. In *Communications: Theory and Research, Proceedings of the First International Symposium*. L. O. Thayer, ed. Springfield: Charles C Thomas, Publisher, pp. 412-428.

McCulloch, W. S. & R. Moreno-Diaz. 1968. On a calculus for triads. *M.I.T. Research Lab. of Electronics. Section Neurophysiology*. QPR

No. 84, pp. 333-346; No. 88, pp. 333-347. Cambridge.

McCulloch, W. S. & W. H. Pitts. 1943. A logical calculus for the ideas immanent in nervous activity. *Bul. Math. Biophys.* 5: 115-133.

Mead, R. 1704. *De Imperio Solis ac Lunae in Corpora Humana, et Morbis inde Oriundis.* London: R. Smith. English translation, 1712. *On the Power and Influence of the Sun and Moon on Humane Bodies; and of the Diseases that Rise from Thence.* London: R. Wellington.

Mead, R. 1747. Advertisement. In his *A Mechanical Account of Poisons, in Several Essays.* 4th edn. London: J. Brindley, p. vi.

Mesmer, F. A. 1779. *Mémoire sur La Découverte du Magnétisme Animal.* Genéve: P. Fr. Didot le jeune. English translation. 1948. *Mesmerism, by Dr. Mesmer.* V. R. Myers, tr. Introductory monograph by G. Frankau. London: Macdonald.

Nelson, J. H. 1951. Shortwave radio propagation correlation with planetary positions. *RCA Review.* 12: 26-34.

Nelson, O. E. Jr. & H. S. Burr. 1946. Growth correlates of electromotive forces in maize seeds. *Proc. Nat. Acad. Sc. U.S.* 32: 73-84.

Newman, H. H., F. N. Freeman & K. K. Holzinger. 1937. *Twins: A Study of Heredity and Environment.* Chicago: University of Chicago Press, p. 212.

Newton, I. 1713. General scholium ff Prop. XLII, Prob. XXII, end of Book III. 2d ed. The System of the World, esp. par. 54: 594. In Sir Isaac Newton's *Mathematical Principles of Natural Philosophy.* 1934. Revision of A. Motte's English version of 1729 by F. Cajori. R. T. Crawford, ed. Berkeley: University of California Press.

Newton, I. 1730. Queries, end of Book III, pp. 313-377. In *Opticks: or, a Treatise of the Reflections, Refractions, Inflections, and Colours of Light* 4th edn. London: William Innys.

Nicholson, S. B. & O. R. Wulf. 1952. The role of quiet days in the mechanics of geomagnetic activity. *Publs. Astron. Soc. Pacific.* 64: 265-271.

Nicholson, S. B. & O. R. Wulf. 1955. Monthly change of diurnal variation of irregular geomagnetic fluctuations. *Science* 122: 379.

Nollet, J. A. 1764. *Recherches sur les Causes Particulieres des Phénomenes Électriques,* et sur les effets nuisibles on avantageux qú on peut en attendre. (Avec approbation & privilege du Roi). Paris: Chez H. L. Guerin, & L. F. Delatour.

Northrop, F. S. C. Jun. 1924. *The Problem of Organization in Biology.* Ph.D. thesis deposited in Harvard University Library, pub. 1931 as his Ch. IV, The living organism. In his *Science and First Principles.* Cambridge: Cambridge University Press & New York: Macmillan, pp. 168-205.

Northrop, F. S. C. Aug. 16, 1928. The Macroscopic Atomic Theory: A physical interpretation of the Theory of Relativity. *J. Phil.* 25: 449-467.

Northrop, F. S. C. Jan. 1930. Two contradictions in current physical theory and their resolution. *Proc. Nat. Acad. Sc. U.S.* 16: 55-68.

Northrop, F. S. C. Apr. 10, 1930. Concerning the philosophical consequences of the Theory of Relativity. *J. Phil.* 27: 197-210.

Northrop, F. S. C. Jul. 1930. The Unitary Field Theory of Einstein and its bearing on the Macroscopic Atomic Theory. *The Monist.* 40: 325-338.

Northrop, F. S. C. 1931. Presented Sep. 1930. The relation between time and eternity in the light of contemporary physics. *Proceedings of the 7th International Congress of Philosophy,* Oxford. G. Ryle, ed. Oxford University Press, London: Humphrey Milford, pp. 100-105.

Northrop, F. S. C. 1931. *Science and First Principles.* Deems Lectures Delivered in New York University in May 1929.

Cambridge: Cambridge University Press & New York: Macmillan. Esp. Ch. IV. The living organism, pp. 168-205; Ch. II. The Theory of Relativity, pp. 55-124; 1979. Preface to 2d edn. Woodbridge: Ox Bow Press, pp. vii-xi.

Northrop, F. S. C. 1936. The mathematical background and content of Greek philosophy. In *Philosophical Essays for Alfred North Whitehead.* London, New York and Toronto: Longmans, Green and Co., pp. 1-40.

Northrop, F. S. C. Apr. 1938. Causality in field physics in its bearing upon biological causation. *Philosophy of Science.* 5: 166-180. Reprinted 1947 in his *The Logic of the Sciences and the Humanities.* New York: Macmillan, Ch. XII, pp. 219-233.

Northrop, F. S. C. 1938. The history of modern physics and its bearing upon biology and medicine. *Yale J. Biol. Med.* 10: 209-232, esp. p. 226.

Northrop, F. S. C. Sep. 1939. The significance of epistemic correlations in scientific method. Read before, and abstract printed for, the *International Congress of Unified Science*, Harvard University.

Northrop, F. S. C. 1939. Body and mind. *Proc. As. Res. Nerv. Ment. Dis.* 19: 99-104: Reprinted 1947 with some modifications in his *The Logic of the Sciences and the Humanities.* New York: Macmillan, Ch. X, pp. 191-199.

Northrop, F. S. C. 1940. The method and theories of physical science in their bearing upon biological organization. *Symposium on Development and Growth.* Reprinted 1947 in his *The Logic of the Sciences and the Humanities.* New York: Macmillan, Ch. VIII. pp. 133-168. Reprinted 1983, Woodbridge: Ox Bow Press, pp. 133-168.

Northrop, F. S. C. 1946. *The Meeting of East and West: An Inquiry Concerning World Understanding.* New York: Macmillan, pp. 442-454, 462, 465, 468, 473, 476, 478, 481, 493. Reprinted 1979.

Woodbridge: Ox Bow Press.

Northrop, F. S. C. 1947. Epistemic correlations and operational definitions. In his *The Logic of the Sciences and the Humanities,* New York: Macmillan, Ch. VII, pp. 119-132.

Northrop, F. S. C. Apr. 23, 1948. The neurological and behavioristic basis of the ordering of society by means of ideas. *Science.* 107: 411-417.

Northrop, F. S. C. 1949. Ch. 14. Einstein's conception of science. In *Albert Einstein: Philosopher-Scientist. Library of Living Philosophers, v.7.* P. A. Schilpp, ed. LaSalle: Open Court & London: Cambridge University Press, pp. 385-408. Einstein's Reply, pp. 683-684.

Northrop, F. S. C. 1958. Introduction In Werner Heisenberg, *Physics and Philosophy: The Revolution in Modern Science.* New York: Harper & Bros. (World Perspectives, v. 19), pp. 1-26.

Northrop, F. S. C. 1959. *The Complexity of Legal and Ethical Experience: Studies in the Method of Normative Subjects.* Boston & Toronto: Little, Brown, esp. pp. 199, 280.

Northrop, F. S. C. 1959. Cultural mentalities and medical science. In *New York Academy of Medicine. Medicine and Anthropology.* Iago Goldston, ed. New York: International Universities Press. (Its Lectures to the Laity, No. 21), pp. 78-107.

Northrop, F. S. C. Nov. 21, 1959. Epistemology in science. In Symposium II: *Field Theory as an Integrator of Knowledge.* Williamsburg: Eastern State Hospital, College of William and Mary and Virginia Society of Clinical Hypnosis. Dodge Room, Phi Beta Kappa Memorial Hall, W & M.

Northrop, F. S. C. Nov. 21, 1959. Epistemology and the psychiatry of the unconscious. In Symposium II: *Field Theory as an Integrator of Knowledge.* Williamsburg: Eastern State Hospital, College of

William and Mary and Virginia Society of Clinical Hypnosis. Dodge Room, Phi Beta Kappa Memorial Hall, W & M.

Northrop, F. S. C. 1960. *Philosophical Anthropology and Practical Politics: A Prelude to War or to Just Law.* New York: Macmillan, esp. pp. 30-31, 32-33, 70, 109-111, 118-119.

Northrop, F. S. C. 1962. Law, language and morals. *The Yale Law J.* 71: 1017-1048.

Northrop. F. S. C. 1970. Ch. 5. The relation between naturalistic scientific knowledge and humanistic intrinsic values in western culture. In *Contemporary American Philosophy: Second Series.* J. E. Smith, ed. London: George Allen & Unwin Ltd., & New York: Humanities Press Inc., pp. 107-151, esp. 119-121.

Northrop, F. S. C. 1985. *The Prolegomena to a 1985 Philosophiae Naturalis Principia Mathematica* which will be able to present itself as a science of the true. Woodbridge: Ox Bow Press.

Northrop, F. S. C. Personal communications and letters. 1947-1986, esp. 1959, 1973-1986.

Northrop, F. S. C. Dec. 28, 1973. Winter Park Conference 1(5); Nov. 16, 1974, Winter Park Conference III (12); March 18, 1975 telephone conversation.

Northrop, F. S. C. Dec. 26-30, 1973. Winter Park Conference, WP I.

Northrop, F. S. C. Nov. 10-16, 1974. WP III.

Northrop, F. S. C. Aug. 8 & Sep. 7, 1974. Letters to Leonard J. Ravitz.

Northrop, F. S. C. Sep. 5, 1974. Letter to J. S. da Fonseca.

Northrop, F. S. C. Jan. 29, 1975. Letter to J. Morgan Thomas, ed. *et al.*

Northrop, F. S. C. March 16, 1975. Telephone conversation.

Northrop, F. S. C. Oct. 26, 1976. Letter to Prof. Dr. Jagdish Mehra, Ph.D. Ecole de Physique, Universite de Genéve, 32 Bd. D'Yvoy, 1211 Geneva 4, Switzerland.

Pattie, F. A. 1956. Mesmer's medical dissertation and its debt to Mead's *De Imperio Solis ac Lunae. J. Hist. Med. Al. Sc.* 11: 275-287.

Pattie, F. A. May 19, 1960. A chapter from 18th-century medicine: the enigmatic character of Franz Anton Mesmer. In Symposium IV: *History of Certain Psychotherapeutic & Forensic Aspects of the Study of Man*. Williamsburg and Ft. Monroe, VA: Eastern State Hospital, College of William and Mary and Virginia Society of Clinical Hypnosis. Recreation Hall, Dunbar 43, Rt 615, ESH.

Pattie, F. A. May 20, 1960. The successors of Mesmer in the 19th century: Puysegur, Elliotson, Braid, Charcot and others. In Symposium IV: *History of Certain Psychotherapeutic & Forensic Aspects of the Study of Man*. Williamsburg and Ft. Monroe: Eastern State Hospital, College of William and Mary and Virginia Society of Clinical Hypnosis. Dodge Room, Phi Beta Kappa Memorial Hall, W & M.

Pattie, F. A. 1993. *Mesmer and Animal Magnetism: A Chapter in the History of Medicine. Hamilton*: Edmonston Publishing.

Pecker, J. C. & W. O. Roberts. 1954. Detection of M-regions in geomagnetic data. *Science*. 120: 721-722.

Penfield, W. 1952. Memory mechanisms. *AMA Arch. Neur. Psychiat.* 67: 178-191.

Petersen, W. F. 1947. *Man • Weather • Sun*. Springfield: Charles C Thomas, Publisher.

Pitts, W. H. & W. S. McCulloch. 1947. How we know universals: the perception of auditory and visual forms. *Bul. Math. Biophys.* 9: 127-147.

Raines, G. N. & J. H. Rohrer. 1955. The operational matrix of psychiatric practice. I. Consistency and variability in interview impressions of different psychiatrists. *Am. J. Psychiat.* 111: 721-733.

Ravitz, L. J. May, 1950. *Standing Potential Correlates of Hypnosis and Narcosis.* Thesis housed in dissertation vault, Sterling Memorial Library, Yale University; abstracted 1950 as Electrometric correlates of the hypnotic state. Science. 112: 341-342; pub. 1951, *AMA Arch. Neur. Psychiat.* 65: 413-436.

Ravitz, L. J. 1951. Daily variations of standing potential differences in human subjects: preliminary report. *Yale J. Biol. Med.* 24: 22-25.

Ravitz, L. J. Fall 1951. The use of DC measurements in psychiatry. *Neuropsychiatry*. 1: 3-12.

Ravitz, L. J. 1952. Fenómenos electrocíclicos y estados emocionales. *Arch. Med. Internal. y Antib. y Quimiot*. 2: 217-252.

Ravitz, L. J. 1952. Electrocyclic phenomena and emotional states. *J. Clin. Exp. Psychopath.* 13: 69-106.

Ravitz, L. J. 1952. Bioelectric correlates of emotional states. *CT State Med. J.* 16: 499-505.

Ravitz, L. J. 1953. In *Annual Review of Hypnosis Literature,* v. 1-2: 44-47. New York: Woodrow Press.

Ravitz, L. J. 1953. Electrodynamic Field Theory in psychiatry. *S. Med. J.* 46: 650-660.

Ravitz, L. J. 1955. Comparative clinical and electrocyclic observations on twin brothers concordant as to schizophrenia, with periodic manifestations of *folie á deux* phenomena. *J. Nerv. Ment. Dis.* 121: 72-87.

Ravitz, L. J. May 1 & 3, 1956. Correlation between DC voltage gradients and clinical changes in a chronic schizophrenic patient, project M-223 (film). Abstracted in *The Scientific Papers of the One Hundred and Twelfth Annual Meeting of the American Psychiatric Association in Summary Form*: 28-C-4. Washington, DC: American Psychiatric Association.

Ravitz, L. J. & C. A. Cuadra. May 3, 1956. Phylogenetic and electrocyclic implications of schizophrenic states. Abstracted in *The Scientific Papers of the One Hundred and Twelfth Annual Meeting of the American Psychiatric Association in Summary Form:* 53. Washington, DC: American Psychiatric Association.

Ravitz, L.J. 1958. How electricity measures hypnosis. Commissioned by the Honorable Frances P. Bolton. *Tomorrow.* 6: 49-56.

Ravitz, L. J. 1959. Application of the electrodynamic field theory in biology, psychiatry, medicine, and hypnosis. I. General survey. *Am. J. Clin. Hyp*. 1: 135-150.

Ravitz, L. J. Nov. 21, 1959. Field Theory in behavior: Logical pragmatic consequence of Field Theory is the application of this construct to the general realm of behavior (including hypnotic behavior). Film II: Field correlates of clinical changes in a chronic schizophrenic patient. In Symposium II: *Field Theory as an Integrator of Knowledge*. Williamsburg: Eastern State Hospital, College of William and Mary and Virginia Society of Clinical Hypnosis. Dodge Room, Phi Beta Kappa Memorial Hall, W & M.

Ravitz, L. J. Dec. 10, 1959. Electric field basis of hypnosis. Force field monitoring in space travel. In Symposium III: *Hypnosis in Office Practice*. Williamsburg: Eastern State Hospital, Williamsburg-James City County Medical Society and Virginia Society of Clinical Hypnosis. Dining Room, Motor House Cafeteria.

Ravitz, L. J. 1960. In memoriam: Richard Sherman Lyman, 1891-1959. *Am. J. Psychiat.* 116: 1055-1056.

Ravitz, L. J. May 19, 1960. Mead-Mesmer tidal constructs reconsidered in the mid-20th century. In Symposium IV: *History of Certain Psychotherapeutic & Forensic Aspects of the Study of Man.* Williamsburg and Ft. Monroe: Eastern State Hospital, College of William and Mary and Virginia Society of Clinical Hypnosis. Recreation Hall, Dunbar 43, Rt 615, ESH.

Ravitz, L. J. Feb. 28, 1961. Relationship of certain paradoxic placebo effects to dissociated states. I & II. Presented at the noonday clinic, Harlan Memorial Hospital; and at the monthly meeting of the Harlan County Medical Society, Harlan.

Ravitz, L. J. July 11, 1961. An electromagnetic screening technique for neuropsychiatric patients. Presented at the Tri-Organization Scientific and Clinical Research Conference, Indiana University Medical Center, Indianapolis.

Ravitz, L. J. Sep.-Oct 1962. Studies of man in the life field. Present experiments show that human behavior as well as many psychic and somatic phenomena are affected by fields. *Main Currents in Modern Thought,* special issue commemorating the Burr-Northrop *Electro-Dynamic Theory of Life.* 19: 13-23.

Ravitz, L. J. Oct. 30, 1962. Read Nov. 10, 1961. History, measurement, and applicability of periodic changes in the electromagnetic field in health and disease. In *Rhythmic Functions in the Living System.* W. Wolf; conference chm. & ed. *An. NY Acad. Sc.* 98(4): 1144-1201.

Ravitz, L. J.. Oct. 30, 1962. Presented Nov. 10, 1961 at New York Academy of Sciences International Conference Banquet. The posited phylogenetic basis of behavior disorders. *Op. cit.,* pp. 1169-1171.

Ravitz, L. J. 1963. W. S. Kroger's *Clinical and Experimental Hypnosis: In Medicine, Dentistry and Psychology.* Book review commissioned by Milton H. Erickson, M.D. *Am. J. Clin. Hyp.* 6: 171-175.

Ravitz, L. J. 1965. L. M. LeCron's *Self-Hypnotism: The Technique and Its Use in Daily Living*. Book review commissioned by Milton H. Erickson, M.D. *Am. J. Clin. Hyp.* 7: 264-265.

Ravitz, L. J. 1966. J. Haley's *Strategies of Psychotherapy.* Book review commissioned by Milton H. Erickson, M.D. *Am. J. Clin. Hyp.* 9: 73-79.

Ravitz, L. J. 1968. The danger of scientific prejudice. Commissioned by Milton H. Erickson, M.D. *Am. J. Clin. Hyp.* 10: 282-303.

Ravitz, L. J. 1970. Electromagnetic field monitoring of changing statefunction, including hypnotic states. *J. Am. Soc. Psychosom. Dent. Med.* 17: 119-129. Reprinted 1972, 1977, 1982, 1988 with some modifications in H. S. Burr, *Blueprint for Immortality: The Electric Patterns of Life*. London & Sudbury, Suffolk: Neville Spearman (bought by The C. W. Daniel Co. Ltd., 1 Church Path, Saffron Walden, Essex CB10 1JP, England), pp. 155-165. In H. S. Burr. 1973 N. Am. edn. *The Fields of Life: Our Links with the Universe,* New York & Toronto: Ballantine, pp. 173-182.

Ravitz, L. J. 1972. Letter to the editor: Notably absent in Dr. Lorrin Koran's article "Psychiatry in Mainland China: History and Recent Status" are the studies of the late Richard S. Lyman, M.D., former Chairman, Department of Neuropsychiatry, Duke University School of Medicine, Durham, NC. *Am. J. Psychiat.* 129: 483-484.

Ravitz, L. J. April 25-26, 1975. Electro-Dynamic Theory of Life of Burr and Northrop—Prophets of the Field Age. Part 1: History and Extensions. In *Proceedings of The Nature and Nurture of Life Conference.* D. D. Harrison, conference director & ed. State University of New York at Stony Brook, pp. 24-29.

Ravitz, L. J. April 25-26, 1975. Part II: Extension of Burr-

Northrop constructs to hypnosis, etc. *Ibid.*, pp. 30-36.

Ravitz, L. J. 1976. Systematic experimental extension of multidimensional relativity field physics to biology and medicine. In *Theoretical Issues in Biological Rhythm Research.* J. Morgan Thomas, ed. *et al.* 4: 28-49.

Ravitz, L. J. 1981. Leaders in contemporary science: Milton Hyland Erickson, 1901-1980. *J. Am. Soc. Psychosom. Dent. Med.* 28: 3-10.

Ravitz, L. J. Sept. 17-20, 1981. Systematic experimental extension of field physics into measurement of emotional and physical states. In The *Proceedings of the Fifth International Conference on Human Functioning*. Century II Convention Ctr., Wichita. Hugh D. Riordan, director & conference chm. Biomedical Synergistics Institute Educational Division of The Olive W. Garvey Center for the Improvement of Human Functioning, Inc. pp. 25-38.

Ravitz, L. J. 1982. EEG correlates of hypnotically-revivified seizures. *J. Am. Soc. Psychosom. Dent. Med.* 29: 128-140.

Redlich, F. C., L. J. Ravitz Jr. & G. H. Dession. 1951. Narcoanalysis and truth. *Am J. Psychiat.* 107: 586-593.

Rosenblueth, A., N. Wiener & J. Bigelow. 1943. Behavior, purpose, and teleology. *J. Phil. Sc.* 10: 18-24.

Rossi, E. L. 1981. Electronic monitoring of catalepsy: a two-factor theory of hypnotic experience, pp. 63-64: Fig. 3: Electronic monitoring of DC body potential during catalepsy, p. 65: Not doing: catalepsy is a form of mental economy utilizing the parasympathetic mode: electrodynamic potential as a measure of an altered receptivity/expression ratio: a proposed definition of therapeutic trance, pp. 195-197. In M. H. Erickson & E. L. Rossi. *Experiencing Hypnosis: Therapeutic Approaches to Altered States.* New York: Irvington Publishers.

Rush, J. H. 1955. A semi-annual periodicity in the beginnings of recurrent magnetic storm series. *Nature.* 175: 517.

Russell, E. W. 1968. The discoveries of Burr and Ravitz: A new way to test personnel. *The Pentagon Seminar "Techniques of Personnel Assessment."* L. M. Ehrmann, ed. Washington, DC 20301: Office of the Secretary of Defense, pp. 121-125.

Russell, E. W. 1971. *Design for Destiny: Science Reveals the Soul.* London: Neville Spearman, bought by The C. W. Daniel Co. Ltd., 1 Church Path, Saffron Walden, Essex CB10 1JP, England. N. Am. edn. 1973. New York & Toronto: Ballantine.

Sambursky, S. 1956. Ch. 5: The world of the atom, and Ch. 6: The world of the continuum. In his *The Physical World of the Greeks.* Translated by Merton Dagut. London: Routledge and Kegan Paul, pp. 105-131, 132-157. See also *Physics of the Stoics. Ibid.* 1959.

Sambursky, S. 1964. Ch. 14: Structural and dynamic elements in the Greek conception of physical reality. In *Cross-Cultural Understanding: Epistemology in Anthropology.* F. S. C. Northrop & Helen H. Livingston eds. New York, Evanston & London: Harper & Row, Publishers, pp. 237-253.

Schafer, D. W. 1960. As-if electroshock therapy by hypnosis. *Am. J. Clin. Hyp.* 2: 225-227.

Sherrington, C. 1951. *Man on His Nature.* 2d edn. Cambridge University Press.

Stetson, H. T. 1947. *Sunspot in Action.* New York: Ronald Press.

Stewart, B. 1883. Hypothetical views regarding the connection between the state of the sun and terrestrial magnetism. In *Encyclopaedia Britannica.,* 9th edn. v.16: 181-184, pars. 115-144. New York: Scribner.

Stichman, E. P. May 20, 1960. Ability to predict changes in electric field states under varying conditions: preliminary report. In Symposium IV: *History of Certain Psychotherapeutic & Forensic Aspects of the Study of Man*. Williamsburg and Ft. Monroe: Eastern State Hospital, College of William and Mary and Virginia Society of Clinical Hypnosis. Roof Garden Terrace, The Chamberlin, Fenwick Rd (US 258), Old Point Comfort, Ft. Monroe.

Stratas, N. E. 1962. Pseudo-electroconvulsive therapy under hypnosis: a controlled pilot study. *Am J. Clin. Hyp*. 5: 62-63.

Tasaki, I. & N. Kamiya. 1950. Electrical response of a slime mold to mechanical and electrical stimuli. *Protoplasma*. 39: 333-343.

Taylor, P. B. 1927. Electromotive force of the cell with transference and theory of interdiffusion of electrolytes. *J. Phys. Chem*. 31: 1478-1500.

Teorell, T. 1935. Studies on the "diffusion effect" upon ionic distribution. I. Some theoretical considerations. *Proc. Nat. Acad. Sc. US*. 21: 152-161.

Thirring, W. 1972. Ch. 4. Gravitation. In *Essays in Physics*, v.4. G. K. T. Conn & G. N. Fowler, eds. London & New York: Academic Press, pp. 125-163.

von Domarus, E. 1967. Ch. XV. The logical structure of mind: an inquiry into the philosophical foundations of psychology and psychiatry. Published posthumously by W. S. McCulloch in *Communications: Theory and Research, Proceedings of the First International Symposium*. L. O. Thayer, ed. Springfield: Charles C Thomas, Publisher, pp. 351-411.

Wolf, S. 1950. Effect of suggestion and conditioning on the action of chemical agents in human subjects. *J. Clin. Invest*. 29: 100-109.

Index to Persons, Places, Institutions and Publications

C

D

E

F

J

K

L

M

N

O

P

R

S

T

U

V

W

Y

For the sake of brevity, only the names of those persons who have most immediately influenced the author's work are included in this Index.

Index to Concepts and Topics

ILLUSTRATIONS AND TABLES

TABLES